hunger
can't
wait

hunger can't wait

by Joseph Sander

Published by

International Minerals & Chemical Corporation

Libertyville, Illinois

table of contents

preface

From 1965 through 1968, I was privileged to serve as the first Chairman of IMC's World Food Production Conferences, and for that reason I have been asked to write this preface. Those were rewarding experiences which I will treasure, as I do the many friendships that began at those meetings. Unfortunately, as chairman of those early Conferences I was given a preponderance of the credit for their inception; actually these Conferences were a natural progression of IMC's corporate growth, coupled with a recognition of our coporate responsibility as the world's leading independent producer of fertilizer raw materials.

During the ten-year history of the Conferences I have been asked repeatedly about IMC's motives in sponsoring this on-going program. Most were well-intentioned, usually revolving around the question, "How can an individual company afford— or justify—the obvious time and expense involved?" Others, perhaps not so kind, have inferred some hidden or devious motivation, usually concluding with the challenge, "What's *really* in it for IMC?" I am delighted to have another opportunity here to answer these questions, as well as to express my own personal feelings about the Conferences.

As I indicated, I feel the World Food Production Conferences were a natural outgrowth of several existing programs that were being carried out domestically by IMC during the early 1960s. These programs started with an annual Customer Advisory Panel in 1961, and grew to include both a Farmer Advisory Board and a Customer Blender Panel in 1964. These meetings led, quite naturally, to an International Management Meeting, also in 1964, which might be credited with setting the stage for the first World Food Production Conference held the following year.

The success of these early panel meetings resulted from the free and open exchange of ideas and experiences between panel members . . . an interchange that proved both profitable and productive to participants, thus encouraging their continued attendance and full participation. It was this same atmosphere that IMC wanted to take overseas, a business area notorious, at that time, for its secretiveness and lack of communications. This open exchange concept has proved to be the cornerstone of the acceptance and continued support enjoyed by the World Food Production Conferences.

The objectives of the Conferences, and of IMC's sponsorship, have always been quite evident to me. The basic objectives are twofold: First, to mobilize agro-industrial leadership in the battle against world hunger and malnutrition; and, second, to publicize the immensity of the world hunger problem, and the solutions offered by the increased use of fertilizers. IMC's rationale was that these agro-industrial leaders represented a strong and heretofore untapped resource in the war on hunger, and that chemical fertilizers offered the most direct and effective answer to the hunger problem. Expanded markets, resulting from increased fertilizer usage, would naturally be available to all producers, and IMC was certain that its demonstrated involvement in those markets would earn it a fair share of the business. This has proved to be a well-founded assumption.

I've always felt that we, in the fertilizer business, had decided advantages over companies marketing other consumer-type products and services. Certainly we're in business to make money. If we weren't, our stockholders would have a valid complaint against management. But, isn't it fortuitous that our product is so necessary to the future of mankind in making possible increased food supplies . . . so advantageous to the farmer through increased production and thus increased farm income . . . and, all the while, it can be a profitable business for producers, manufacturers, and retailers in supplying this vital production-increasing input? The viewpoint that IMC's sponsorship of these Conferences is out of character, or at odds with other corporate goals, is obviously false.

It is not necessary for me to point out that the Conferences have been successful. They have accomplished what they set out do do. They have attracted—and continue to attract—top level participation from throughout the world. At this very moment, we are considering expanding our efforts in other regions and to other peoples of the globe. To fail to mention that our own corporate growth has kept pace with our highest expectations over this same period would be amiss. During the ten-year span of the Conferences, IMC has become a billion-dollar-plus company . . . a company that, I feel, has set some extremely high corporate standards in meeting its self-recognized social responsibilities.

Yet, the real challenges offered by the World Food Production Conferences are only beginning to be recognized today. Already the Conferences and their participants have agreed that today mankind possesses the know-how to produce enough food to feed the world's burgeoning population. Yet, the real test of the Conferences' effectiveness lies ahead. That will come when this message—and the necessary inputs to make it a fact—reach each and every farmer . . . in each participant's homeland.

Both IMC and I pledge our continued support and assistance toward this goal.

Anthony E. Cascino
Executive Vice President
International Minerals & Chemical Corporation

introduction

What this book *is* will, of course, unfold during the reading. But it is, perhaps, important to let the reader know at the outset what it is *not*. The subject of man, his need for food, and what can be done to obtain it is virtually without beginning and certainly without ending. No single volume could encompass the tale. This one, surely, has no such intent.

This volume is neither a history of agriculture nor a history of fertilizer, though it very much concerns both. Nor is it a record of the world's major famines, although it also concerns hunger and malnutrition. And neither is it a book on the population crisis, except insofar as the growth of world population acts as a spur and a target for the increased production of food.

The story that emerges in the following pages is the story of one company's response to the world food problem, an exciting approach found within its own area of expertise and influence. And it is one that has already played a significant role in increasing worldwide awareness of the problem of hunger.

International Minerals & Chemical Corporation developed its unique role in an unorthodox manner that is especially significant because its actions not only brought new focus to worldwide concerns for increasing the supply of food, but seemed as well to signal an unprecedented hope for aiding the world's farmers to feed an ever-growing population.

The birth of agriculture and domestication of the first animals is believed to have occurred about 8,000 B.C. in the region we know today as the Middle East. This provided the triggering mechanism for the development of civilization as we understand it today. From agriculture's ability to support more rapid growth of population centers grew government, trade, and commerce.

All this did not emanate from one center, of course, and within a relatively short period of time, agriculture had developed spontaneously in other, widely separated regions—North China, Mexico, and Peru.

While that story is vast, it contains few specific details. What is known is widely known. We will not venture far into it within the pages of this book.

Similarly, there is a long human history of famine and starvation, which has been part of man's heritage from the very beginning. Just since the written documentation of famine, the price in human lives has been astronomical and continues fearfully into the present time.

Historically, famines have originated in the effects of weather, war, and diseases . . . which remain among its causes to the present time. And yet another cause that has risen from the traditional ranks to become a leading and critical factor is the growth of population. Despite our contemporary level of social development and sophistication in the ability to minimize the effects of war, ameliorate many of the harsh effects of weather, and reduce the impact of plant diseases, the potential human damage of famine has risen drastically in recent years because of the faster-growing population levels.

The crisis factor of population is the subject of many books and studies. Attempts to curb the growth rate are, for the most part, matters of moral and political decision. They are not agricultural in nature, and we do not attempt to solve them within these pages. However, population does place a demand on the agriculture of the world and figures in a necessarily large number of considerations relative to the increased production of food. Population is certainly a factor in any equation in which the amount of food produced is divided by the numbers of people who will consume it.

IMC's answer to the world food problem is to produce more food. And that is the major subject of this book. It takes a pragmatic approach to increasing food production from existing arable land. It sees as the easiest, swiftest and most effective method an increase in worldwide fertilizer usage—and following that, pest controls, new farming methods, new varieties of plants and farm mechanization.

As those steps are fulfilled, it will be necessary to develop new agricultural lands that can be brought under the plow economically. The best land is, of course, already in use nearly everywhere, and additional land will be marginal and expensive to develop. There is yet much unknown about the utilization of so-called virgin lands—the forests, swamps, and sandy desert areas. Large-scale research is required, not only to unlock the secrets of these areas of potential food production, but to open up agriculture to greater productivity by increasing crop yields, extending growing seasons, revitalizing soil and other potential means of adding measurably to the world supply of food. IMC's commitment is to support more, not less, research of this nature.

Through the pages of this book will unfold the dramatic story of how IMC, one industrial corporation, has liberated its viewpoint on corporate responsibility and moved from narrow business concerns to a much broader understanding. The story reveals how a company discovered that its business goals and mankind's social goal of providing sufficient food for all the people of the earth were harmonious . . . and what it did about that discovery.

This book will document the development of corporate insight into the manner in which programs designed to aid customers were finally perceived as a means of increasing the food supply of the world. It will show how private meetings with customers—manufacturers, dealers, and farmers—formed the basis for the first continuing series of world food production conferences. It is these important conferences, now entering their second decade of existence, which largely form the basis of the book.

The author wishes to acknowledge gratefully the openness of access to the complete conference files granted by IMC, together with the insights provided by its executives. Special thanks go to Barry Kraemer of IMC for the warmth of his creative concerns in developing the beautiful design of this book and its jacket.

And—above all—gratitude must be expressed to my wife Kelly, who put up with me lovingly during the difficulties of writing, and to the many, many exciting and wonderful people from nations around the world, whose dedicated efforts as conferees of the World Food Production Conferences provided the vital substance on which this book is built.

And for whatever contribution this volume makes to the fight against hunger, I am most grateful to IMC for having given me this opportunity to serve in that struggle.

Joseph Sander

hunger
...what about it?

How man handles the problem of human hunger today is, to most of us, very nearly the measure of man himself. The sense-dulling regularity with which swollen-bellied children appear on television, and the very numbers that accumulate to make newspaper headlines, diminish them into digits in an inhuman equation. The plight of hunger has so numbed us that we just don't want to think about it anymore. No one can deal meaningfully with the death of 10 to 20 millions each year from hunger-related causes, or the fact that more than a billion humans go to bed every night suffering the pangs of hunger.

No one even wants to think about it. Certainly not those among the general public who feel burdened enough in their own lives. Not those embroiled in government bureaucracies around the world. Not those in industry and commerce. And that's not surprising; no one who didn't have to, ever wanted to look at it. But those who had to, *couldn't* look at it, because they *were* it. "We know," said the world, over and over, "we know. And we wish there were something we could do about it."

ABOUT IT:

The United Nations Food and Agriculture Organization estimated that as much as half the entire world's population experienced hunger or suffered malnutrition during the year 1964.

During the year 1964, the people of 37 major countries had average energy intake levels below the minimum recommended to maintain normal physical activity and health. Thirty-five of these countries had populations with serious deficiencies in animal protein or total protein. These included mainland China, India, Pakistan and Indonesia, which alone contain more than half the population of all *the developing nations.*

That was the condition of the world when, in an unusual move, a group of unusual people joined together around an oversize table in Hong Kong in the spring of 1965. They had come from the Philippines, South Korea, Australia, New Zealand, Taiwan, India, Japan and Hong Kong itself, all parts of the Far Eastern quadrant of the world. That quadrant holds two-thirds of the world's population, but less than one-half of its arable land. Importantly, too, that quadrant was growing in population more rapidly than any other segment of the world, with a projected increase of 50 percent for the short 15 year period ahead.

Most of those gathered had never met before, though some had knowledge of one another through reading business, scientific, and agricultural journals. Among them were men of various backgrounds and disciplines, carrying titles of Doctor, or General, or corporation executive. They were people whose lives, in many cases, had been devoted to industry, farming, finance, education, economics, and other agriculturally related disciplines.

They met to discuss hunger. They were drawn together because of their concern about it.

ABOUT IT:

"We live in a world of 3.4 billion human beings, half of whom do not have enough to eat. Population will increase as much in the next 35 years as it has since the beginning of time. Today's teenager will live most of his life in a world of 5 to 6 billion people while, by the year 2000, there will be 5 billion people crowded into those areas of the world where hunger is already common."

. . . from conference proceedings, 1965

In a sense, the people who gathered in Hong Kong in 1965 were there to participate in a dedication. They had much related knowledge in common. They knew there were areas of the world that produced more than 5,000 pounds of rice to the acre, and they knew there were areas with very rich and scarce arable land that were only producing 500 pounds, or less, to the acre.

They knew that fertilizer had, in some countries, boosted crop production by as much as 95 percent without changing a single other farming technique.

They knew that—at the latest U.N. count—there were approximately 170 countries in the world, and that of those only 112 used chemical fertilizers. They also knew that only a small number of those countries processed, or manufactured, those fertilizers.

And they were well aware that only the peoples of North America, Europe, Japan, Australia, and New Zealand were adequately fed and that the remaining 80 percent of the world's population had either deficient or marginal food supplies.

The people around the table in Hong Kong represented, collectively, 80 percent of the total fertilizer production in the Asia-Pacific area. They knew all these things, and more. They were people of authority and decision. Looking backwards, subsequent conference proceedings said of this initial gathering, and a sister meeting the next month in Latin America, that "1965 will be commemorated for many centuries to come as being the key year in which finally, and unequivocally, the world recognized that it was living in a condition of serious deficiency in food."

This meeting in Hong Kong, then, began the first World Food Production Conference, an initial gathering not only of people, but of forces. The participants were there in recognition of the problem of hunger, and to gather and focus their forces to do something about it.

ABOUT IT:

In 1965 the average daily food consumption in India was only 400 grams of cereal per person. Population was 450 million and was increasing at a rate of 10 million per annum.

That increase is the equivalent of a new Australia every year, more than the equivalent of a new Venezuela every year. The massive population surge in India represents one-seventh of the entire world's annual population increase. Despite projected Indian food production increases of 50 percent over the next six years, the food intake per capita was only expected to increase by less than 10 percent in that same period—due to the extremely rapid increase of population.

The sponsor of this first World Food Production Conference in Hong Kong was from the United States. It had extended invitations to those assembled to meet in their own quadrant of the globe in a desire to begin the reasoning process that could lead to an attack on the problem of hunger. It was possible, the sponsor felt, to call upon the earth for more benefits, as man had done before, laboriously, through all the centuries since the beginning of agriculture.

Since the conferees were each specialists, as was the sponsor, it was felt that together they were in a unique position to focus attention on the problem and to do something about it.

ABOUT IT:

Agriculture began in the brain of man; he perceived the need to look at what he saw as reality differently, in order to change it. Late Stone Age man had thought deeply about what he found around him, and how he could affect what he found, so as to make human life more regular, internal, and less terrifying. This early thought doubtless involved man's first concept of the future as something that needed to be planned for. That concept further suggested that if man could activate his ideas and work with the earth, he could alter certain life-giving processes.

The activation of those ideas is what led to agriculture.

The sponsor of the first World Food Production Conference was International Minerals and Chemical Corporation, known worldwide as IMC. The reasons for its optimism about affecting world food production were quite clear.

IMC was mainly in the business of producing fertilizer raw materials for agriculture. As the world's largest private corporation engaged in such an activity, it had both the practical and the scientific basis for understanding how the application of chemical fertilizers could enhance the productivity of the soil. Growing more food was, it felt, the contribution it was best able to make towards the solution of the world hunger problem. It knew that something could be done about it.

ABOUT IT:

In the early 1970s the worst drought in the recorded history of Africa left a devastated area 4,000 miles long, from Senegal to Ethiopia. The peanut crop of Nigeria fell to only one-third the nor-

mal yield. Nearly 100,000 humans died in the Welo and Tigre prov-
inces of Ethiopia. Some died by drowning in Desse, the capital of
Welo province, too weakened by hunger to raise their heads from
the gutters in which they lay when a rainstorm finally did break in
the area. More than 3,000 elephants, lions, giraffes, and buffalo
starved to death in the Waza National Park of the Cameroons. Car-
casses of cattle, sheep, camels, and goats littered the Danakil desert
in Harar province; as a result of the drought-caused ruin the nomadic
tribesmen there may die out, and disappear as a race. Numbers of
human dead of the Danakil were found with dirt in their stomachs—
they had been reduced to licking the earth for moisture.

IMC's optimism about the possibility of increasing world food
production was deeply rooted in history. More than half of the
prodigious increases in crop production—nearly legendary increases that had made the United States the world's largest
food producer—was due to the use of fertilizer alone. The principle of feeding and replenishing the earth, in order to draw
more food from it, was well established.

But it had not always been so. It seems an obvious fact today, but fewer than 200 years ago it was unknown.

It was a European named von Liebig who began our contemporary understanding of growing more food in less space.
Nearly all modern knowledge and thought on this subject trace
back to this man's life work. He wrote:

"If I can impress the farmer with the principles of plant nutrition, soil fertility, and the causes of soil exhaustion, one
of the tasks of my life will be accomplished."

He was fortunate with his life and that task was accomplished, at least in part, and at least in principle. His discovery that
the earth had to be fed in order for the earth to feed man did
impress many and the principle, at least, of plant nutrition has
been universally accepted since. Man, in many parts of the
world at that time, was hungry; plant nutrition, von Liebig felt
could do something about it.

ABOUT IT:

A million-and-a-half people perished, mostly by starvation, during
the great potato famine in Ireland between 1845 and 1849. Many
wandered the roads, and died. in the ditches alongside. Typhus ap-
peared, and entire villages of carrion became rotting cemeteries.

Von Liebig came upon the world at a time when the land was in need of relief from the continuous drain upon it. There was great concern for food in the world, but land was clearly beginning to fail. Areas that had, historically, produced great crops and supported large populations beyond the memory of the oldest person, had become less productive and, in some cases, no longer able to do anything about it.

ABOUT IT:

In 1878, a famine in China caused the deaths of 9,500,000 people. A Baptist Missionary, Rev. Timothy Edwards, wrote in his first-hand account of the disaster:

"That people pull down their homes, sell their wives and daughters, eat roots and carrion, clay and leaves, is news nobody wonders at. It is the regular thing . . .

"The poorest people are dependent on willow and elm leaves, elm bark, and the various weeds . . . All the elm trees about many of the villages are stripped of this bark as high as the starving people can manage to get; they would peel them to the top but haven't the strength . . ."

At the time of von Liebig's birth, there was another man living whose importance still weighs heavily over the question of whether the earth's surface can continue to provide for a rapidly expanding population. That man was Thomas Robert Malthus. He was, in fact, a good-natured, amiable person, but he shattered the utopian illusions of his time, and history so marked him with eternal gloom that it is hard to imagine that he ever smiled.

The son of a country gentleman in the English tradition, who was also a friend of Rousseau, young Malthus was schooled in the goodness of man by a succession of tutors. But the beautiful world idealists saw emerging from the French Revolution seemed a bitter delusion to him. He found himself unable to rejoice at an expanding, prosperous England of 9 million people, building churches and caring for their poor, because in his view such apparently happy times could only bring ultimate overpopulation, and its consequent misery.

Malthus became a teacher and a clergyman, though he spoke with difficulty from a cleft palate and harelip. He was dividing his time between Cambridge and a curacy in Surrey when he wrote his first, "Essay on the Principle of Population."

Plato, Aristotle, and Ben Franklin had all treated the subject before him, but it remained for mathematician Malthus to cast, in 1798, the geometrical progression of population—"1, 2, 4, 8, 16, 32, 64, 128, 256 . . . " against an arithmetical increase in food supply—"1, 2, 3, 4, 5, 6, 7, 8, 9 . . ." and seal man's doom with perfect logic. He wrote:

"I think I may fairly make two postulata.

"First, that food is necessary to the existence of man.

"Second, that the passion between the sexes is necessary, and will remain nearly in its present stage . . .

"Assuming then, my postulata as granted, I say that the power of population is indefinitely greater than the power in the earth to produce subsistence for man.

"Population, when unchecked, increases in a geometrical ratio. Subsistence increases only in an arithemetical ratio. A slight acquaintance with numbers will show the immensity of the first power as compared with the second.

"By that law of our nature which makes food necessary to the life of man, the effects of these two unequal powers must be kept equal.

"This implies a strong and constantly operating check on population from the difficulty of subsistence . . . The race of plants, and the race of animals shrink under this great restrictive law. And the race of man cannot, by any efforts of reason, escape from it. Among plants and animals its effects are waste of seed, sickness, and premature death. Among mankind, misery and vice. The former, misery, is an absolutely necessary consequence of it. Vice is a highly probable consequence . . . I see no way by which man can escape from the weight of this law which pervades all animated nature . . ."

Malthus' doctrine touched off an immediate storm of controversy. England's Prime Minister Pitt withdrew from Parliament a Poor Bill that would have made relief payments proportionate to the size of families. Karl Marx denounced Malthus as "a shameless sycophant of the ruling classes." Disraeli entered the fray with his biting satire, and Dickens' Scrooge-like characters began invoking Malthus' viewpoint in the defense of their inhumanity.

The outcry moved Malthus to five years of study, travel, and reflection, followed by a second edition of his Essay, in which he admitted a glimmer of hope for mankind. His Essay went through six editions, but it was too late to lift the long shadow he had cast, and to this day it remains a symbol of darkness and despair.

He was a man whose idea took hold of the modern world with the clenched teeth of a bulldog, and has hung on persistently ever since. He represents, even today, a polar band of the spectrum of thought centering on the formation of an equation that could accurately state the true relationship between hunger, food and population. At the opposite polar extreme of this spectrum of thought, von Liebig would be represented.

Justus von Liebig came from peasant stock. His father had settled in the German town of Darmstadt and ran a kind of drugstore where young von Liebig enjoyed a boyhood acquaintance with chemicals. Weak in school, he was apprenticed to a pharmacy in the village of Heppenheim at fourteen. There, von Liebig's secret experiments with fulminate of mercury blew the roof off the pharmacy and abruptly terminated his apprenticeship.

But this did not destroy the youth's fascination with chemistry and plant life, which drew him to the Universities of Bonn and Erlangen, and on to the Sorbonne to study under Gaylussac, Dulong and Thenard. His first lecture (ironically, on fulminate of mercury) so impressed Alexander von Humboldt that the great man was moved to write of the young chemist: *"Ce s'era un professeur qui honerera notre patrie"*—one professor who will honor our fatherland.

The prophecy was fulfilled. Von Liebig first detected phosphate and potash in the ashes of burned plants, and found ammonia in the vapors. He tried all three in a barren plot of ground. It soon became a wonder of fertility, and his star rose quickly to light the dawning sky of agricultural chemistry over a century ago.

Von Liebig lived from 1803 to 1873, teaching for over 50 years, and profoundly influencing the learning of many of the world's best chemists. Wagner, Prianischnikov, Mayer and other great chemists carried on the work that von Liebig had begun, proving for all time the importance of chemistry to what one colleague called, "the heathens of agriculture who did not want to believe."

As early as the 1840s von Liebig was urging farmers to recycle all human and animal waste to the land. He knew that would lead to fertility, but did not believe it was the only way. "If we could produce elsewhere," he wrote, "the substances which give to the manure this value in agriculture, we should not need the manure."

He further wrote that, "It is quite indifferent, for our purpose, whether we supply the ammonia in the form of urine, or in that of a salt derived from coal-tar; whether we derive the phosphate of lime from bones, apatite, or fossils." And he had proved it with his famously fertile demonstration plots.

His colleague Wagner's classic soil-fertility experiments made Darmstadt a cradle of agricultural chemistry, where others came to compare notes. There, on their weekend walks in later years, they saw mighty chemical plants building up along the Rhine, where Haber and Bosch had synthesized nitrogen.

For them, even then, von Liebig's prophetic words were as meaningful as they are to the world today. "There will be a time," he said, "when the fields will be fed with substances produced by chemical industries, and containing the substances indispensable for plants." Von Liebig was a chemist who knew of hunger, and of chemistry's ability to do something about it.

ABOUT IT:

An English writer described existing conditions in 1844:
"Fully one-third of our population subsist almost entirely, or rather starve, upon potatoes alone; another third have, in addition to this edible, oaten or inferior wheaten bread, with one or two meals of fat pork, or the refuse of the shambles, per week; while a considerable majority of the remaining third seldom are able to procure an ample daily supply of good butcher's meat or obtain the luxury of poultry from year to year.

"On the continent of Europe, population is still in a worse condition: fish; soups made from herbs; stuff called bread, made from every variety of grain, black, brown and sour, such as no Englishman could eat; olives, chestnuts, the pulpy saccharine fruits, roots,

stalks and leaves, and not infrequently the bark of trees; sawdust, blubber, train oil with frogs and snails make up a good part of the food of the greater portion of the inhabitants of Europe."

Von Liebig and Malthus, between them, account for the two gigantic bases of interest in agriculture. The difference between them lay in the realm of concept. One concept sensed the potential of the unsprung earth, and learned how to read its music and make it play its tune melodiously and unendingly. Von Liebig had responded to the land, and it to him. He understood, too, that truth was encapsulated in principles, and it was the principles that he wanted to teach. Not absolutes, but principles, and to the extent that they were learned, the world has been able to increase its ever-growing supply of food.

On the other side, Malthus' view has never stopped being a concern, reconstituted as a threatening flag that some set to wave again over today's world. It is a flag of doom, signalling surrender to a theoretical concept of absolute truth that could easily become self-fulfilling. One would only need ignore von Liebig to ensure the success of Malthus.

For there was no question that increasing the ability to provide also increased the number of mouths to provide for. From the sun of optimism that von Liebig represented, the shadow cast has been that of Malthus. Ever since, man has concerned himself further, in search of the truth upon which to build a more workable equation for dealing with the problem represented by food, hunger and population.

What had happened was that von Liebig had let the genie out of the bottle. The basic principle had been proved . . . that man could reconceive the reality in which he had been thrust, and utilize the resources of himself and the world around him in new ways that would help propel him forward. The future *could* be different than the past. That was the basic discovery, and what that meant was that now *thought* could be projected forward faster, and with more meaningful results, than could the humdrum practical lessons of *time*.

Had Malthus conceived in this pattern, or examined this concern, he would, perhaps, have found a matching equation of optimism to offset his despair. For it was observably true that progress forged by increasing man's understanding of his past, is largely arithmetical. But the projection of thought into the future can be done exponentially, which can move it even faster than the geometric progression Malthus found applicable to population growth. Therefore, it may be argued that the potential existed, even then, for the virtually limitless production of food. Man hadn't yet the technology, but that was on the way. And he hadn't yet the answers in his head, but he was then beginning to unfold the mysteries of the human brain, and was already sensing its virtually limitless ability to expand conceptual power. And it was knowledge of this principle and this history that underlay the optimism that IMC felt about world food production.

And optimism was needed, because there were few apparent reasons for it. World population had so increased that, by 1964, two-thirds of the world was dependent for its food supply on the precarious balance between the growth of food-output and the growth of population. Generally speaking, population increases in those areas had outpaced the food supply four to one. The struggle between the optimism of von Liebig and the dark pessimism of Malthus became fully engaged, and the first clear indications of how the struggle would go in contemporary reality—after having been so long debated in theory—were anxiously awaited.

A glimmering of the severity of the problem was indicated by figures from the northern half of South America which, just prior to 1964, revealed an addition in one year of nearly 4 million persons to its population, while food production in the area was, at best, unchanged from a year earlier.

But by no means was the problem felt in South America alone. For the same period, the United Nations Commission on Asia and the Far East reported food production for that area as a whole increased only by one-half of one percent, against a nearly two-and-one-half percent rise in population.

At the practical and immediate level, the first indicators seemed to lean heavily toward Malthus.

But IMC knew that agriculture was not asleep, nor standing still. New strains of wheat and rice were beginning their demonstration of how production of grain could be increased. Fertilizer was becoming re-understood, and the brain of man was seeking further and further into the future for means of growing more food.

The world had clearly evolved into an unbalanced situation of "have" and "have not" nations. Aside from the many other questions of modern industrial development and overall quality of life, this description has essentially come to mean "fed" and "not fed" nations.

And this has to do with more than agriculture, for the countries that are unable, for reasons of poor agricultural development, to feed their populations are, for the most part, countries that are too poor overall to purchase sufficient foodstocks or fertilizers from those nations that have quantities to offer for export sale.

A look backward at the traditional and historical role of agriculture in the feeding of the world . . . lays the burden at the door of agriculture today. Food has always been the only answer to man's most basic hunger. Its production and distribution have been largely responsible for the development of modern civilization. Unless the means are found to resolve the problems faced by the hungry of the world today, civilization, as we know it, must soon end, and mankind will then have to undergo a change in its basic consideration of itself.

In the sense of what is important to every thinking, feeling, perceiving human being, there is now a frightening apparition hovering over the world that presses hard on our sense of humanity. If it presses much harder, or much longer unchecked, it will greatly affect our sense of self. So it thereby becomes a matter of great human self-interest that we now begin to conceive the problem somewhat differently.

We seem to be at the point in human development where Malthus and von Liebig intersect. And we are still faced with the same old question, "Must we limit food and therefore people?" Have we struggled these many thousands of years to reach the highest potential of man, only to find that we are there? It hardly seems thinkable that what we are today is the most we can be.

Clearly, we have only a limited time in which to act. Gradually the focus is beginning to narrow. Formerly abstract questions are becoming concrete. As we stand at the crossroads between Malthus and von Liebig, we face—in contemporary terms—the same situation that man has always faced. And today, as always, it will be the mark of man how he deals with his situation.

The future requires that we think of man and the world efficiently. Efficiency for hunters and gatherers was a thousand acres per person. Efficiency for agriculture immediately reduced this need to two or three acres per person.

From that early reshaping of man's food supply came a vital solution that altered the life of man. It is again time to reshape the production of food in terms of man's responsibility to the future of man. If we do otherwise, we will not long be able to hold on to all that we have believed about ourselves as human beings.

To salvage the thrust of man, and the self-image of humanism that he has thus far developed on his trek through the universe, it is necessary to universally assume the portentous postulate:

THE WORLD'S GREATEST PROBLEM IS HUNGER

THE WORLD'S GREATEST NEED IS FOOD'

the responsibility of minding your own business

The force of population growth exerts tremendous pressure on agriculture. With the present growth rate of 70 million people, the farmers of the world would need to bring between 30 and 40 million new acres under cultivation—every year—at today's production levels—even to maintain the present low levels of nutrition that are spread so widely around the globe. The population of the world is now doubling every 40 years, and the skills, knowledge and materials required to maintain a similar growth in food production are not being put to work at a similar pace.

This is explainable, in part, only by paradox. Food supply is based on the growth of plants. Of all the earth's surface, the place where plants grow most profusely is the area between the Tropics of Cancer and Capricorn. And yet is is precisely that area of the world—best suited to plant growth—that is the scene of the greatest hunger, like a great black sash tied around the world at its middle.

The irony is that the areas of plenteous rainfall and continuous warmth turn out to be the least favorable in terms of soil fertility. For most tropical soils are naturally low in plant food, due to rapid oxidization of the organic matter and continual leaching of the soil.

To give everyone now living a diet sufficient to meet known minimum nutritional needs for ordinary physical and mental activity, we would have to double food production. And to *improve* world nutrition, food production would have to double again by 1980—and quadruple by the year 2000.

All of these factors were part of the reasoning behind the first World Food Production Conferences. These conferences were held in the geographic regions of greatest concern; the first was in the Asia/Pacific region, the second, a month later, in Latin America. This latter conference brought people together representing food production concerns in an area extending 12,900 kilometers from north to south with an existing population of 225 million that was projected to double within 20 years.

Observed a spokesman for the conference sponsor, "In this conference, we are concerned, as our main objective, with the problem of producing enough food to feed these people."

How IMC, a corporation with traditional capitalist dedication, came to have a concern for the objective of feeding people, marks an interesting development in corporate history.

The World Food Production Conferences have been, since their inception in 1965, hard-nosed, pragmatic, and practical affairs. Yet, as we shall see, they were rooted deeply in a company philosophy that had been forming for more than ten years. Even a large private corporation cannot suddenly project such a conference from nowhere . . . and indeed IMC had not.

THE CORPORATE MOLECULE:

IMC is a corporation involved in many industrial sectors. Its major agricultural efforts center on the mining of minerals and chemicals which are then processed into fertilizers to be fed back into the earth, in different locations and different concentrations, depending on various soil and plant requirements. These industrial and business processes follow a very intricate chain of events, each stage of which must be organized and founded on sound economic principles.

Because the process is both complex and cumbersome, it traditionally has functioned most efficiently in those parts of the world where the most widespread education in modern affairs has made it possible. Communications and resources were what brought the end products of a modern corporation to its customers. The corporate molecule was initially formed to function most effectively in those circumstances.

In Caracas, in 1965, the first Latin American Food Production Conference assembled conferees representing food production interests in Venezuela, Mexico, Brazil, and other Caribbean nations. Between them, delegates represented a major pecentage of the fertilizer production capability of Latin America.

The problem of capital to finance the expanded use of fertilizer was a major topic. The vice-president of the host company observed: "The limitation of capital, both working capital and non-working capital, has been a restriction for most of the fertilizer industry in all parts of the world. One of the things that we learned in the United States, where the same problem existed, was that we had to develop ways and means by which we could more intelligently acquaint the sources of capital, chiefly the local bankers, with the great potential of the fertilizer industry so that they would be more willing to extend capital in that direction. This is a real problem. It's also a problem on the farm; the single biggest problem cited by the farmers of North America was the limitation of capital."

The conferees agreed that the raising of money to finance farmers was high among the practical obstacles to increased food production, and this problem figured largely in conference proceedings.

Until about ten years prior to the World Food Production Conference, IMC had been a "traditional" corporation. Its business was basically the mining of potash and phosphate—raw materials for fertilizer production—and its traditional corporate position was that it had properly concluded its business with delivery of goods and receipt of payment. From that point on, it considered the life of those minerals on their indirect route back into the earth was none of its business. There were others down the line who had their own specific ventures built around just such concerns.

Traditionally, from the point of delivery on it became the responsibility of the purchaser to do as he wanted with the product. He could dispose of it under any conditions he so desired; and if the purchaser wasn't knowledgeable and efficient, failed to profit, and collapsed as a result, that was entirely his problem.

This was, essentially, traditional industry practice, which IMC followed.

Yet, in Caracas in 1965 a major executive of IMC was addressing the conference on Food Production saying, "We must say to each other over and over again: never before has mankind dared to accept the challenge of providing enough food for all. It was always accepted that the good Lord made poor people in greater numbers because He loved them and that, for some reason, they ought to starve to death.

"But we don't, at this day and age, dare to take this view. Every human being born in this world deserves three full meals a day. And we have the resources, we have the ability . . . all we need is the determination, the tenacity to stick to it."

"Traditional practices," he added, "are not fast enough, will not make the rapid strides necessary. So we're going to have to depart from the known and go into the unknown.''

That was, of course, just what IMC was already doing with its sponsorship of the Conference, going into the unknown . . . departing from the traditional. Why? What had happened to shift the traditional course of a major corporation?

THE CORPORATE MOLECULE:

Approximately ten years earlier, the corporate leadership of IMC began to question the validity of the traditional practice of considering responsibility to have ended with the delivery of product. It came to appreciate the fact that any traditional behavior which has been in existence for a period of time is in danger of becoming shopworn and obsolete. IMC reexamined the nature and structure of both its industry and its business; it came to the conclusion that logically it shared in the responsibility for the task that von Liebig had claimed for his life—that of impressing the farmer with "the principles of plant nutrition, soil fertility, and the causes of soil exhaustion . . ."

Largely as a result of this reexamination, IMC then restated its corporate beliefs along the following lines: That IMC, to grow and prosper, to help make the fertilizer industry a dynamic, vibrant one, and to contribute to the health and progress of agriculture all over the world, would have to adopt the philosophy that nothing it does is sacred, that it will constantly seek and pursue a better way, and that no matter how successful it may have been yesterday, today it would wake up asking itself, "How can we do it better?"

In this spirit, IMC corporate leadership decided that its obligation and responsibility did *not* end when the firm sold a product to the customer. The management accepted the new perception that its responsibility continued and that all of the resources then possessed, and the many more that would, in time, be added to the corporate entity, should be made available to the purchaser of their product so that he could become more efficient, more profitable, and better able to contribute to the prosperity of agriculture.

From that time on, IMC has made every resource, every discipline, every professional it employs, available on request to any customer anywhere in the world. From this beginning

IMC felt a natural sense of pride in its new philosophy, and its implementation. The corporation believed it was performing its rightful responsibility to its industry—and to agriculture.

THE CORPORATE MOLECULE:

After a few years, however, IMC became less satisfied with its efforts. Allegiance with von Liebig's cause was only partial; the company was teaching the principles of soil fertility, all right, and doing a good job of it. But it was not teaching the farmer.

IMC realized it was not enough just to work with the fertilizer manufacturer—to assist, aid, and cooperate with him. It came to understand that the job could not be considered complete until the farmers of the world had been included in the new orbit.

What IMC did then (this was still some years before the World Food Production Conferences) was to arrange with *its* customers to go out arm-in-arm, so to speak, directly to the farmer. Together, they could collectively use their resources, ideas, people, and equipment to help make the farmers of the world more efficient, more effective, and more profitable.

So, again, a comfortable sense of fulfilled responsibility overtook IMC. It was saying to itself, "Now we have completed the cycle, done justice to von Liebig, and are fulfilling the responsibilities of our industry."

THE CORPORATE MOLECULE:

Those were the beginning sequences of the activities that have characterized IMC's development of a new corporate philosophy; one that could enable it to deal adequately with its corporate sense of responsibility.

As a result, IMC has been able to make itself more meaningful and more helpful to everyone among those it serves and with whom it comes in commercial contact.

At about the same period, IMC took another step, this time a domestic one. It developed what it called an Advisory Panel from among those with whom it had commercial contact. This panel met once a year for about a day-and-a-half for the purpose of free, uninhibited, frank, open, honest, and courageous discussion. The end result was a positive feeling by all participants of being better equipped—either individually or as part of a complex—to be more effective in helping the agricultural industries within the United States produce more efficiently and economically.

To make this concept really effective and meaningful to its participants, IMC realized, it must be prepared to act on the suggestions engendered by the meetings with sincere and genuine interest. It could not be just window dressing, or it would benefit no one. Worse, it would betray the sense of responsibility that impelled them in the first place to bring knowledgeable people together to spark ideas, and help develop mechanisms for their application.

It seemed obvious to IMC that if it were not prepared to act in that manner, then its customers would quickly tire of meeting each year, correctly perceiving that IMC's interest had been only vain, superficial, and insincere.

THE CORPORATE MOLECULE:

But something important and apparently irreversible had happened within the company. Not only had the output of its philosophical reexamination proven meaningful to the company and the industry which it served, but it also indicated that "corporate molecules" could actually re-form differently around the same basic internal structures. Moreover, it could—without radically changing any of the structures within which it operated—alter the course of corporate direction toward perceived goals.

That perception formed the nucleus of the IMC hope of reshaping its agricultural business molecules. While the company never lost its zeal for selling its product profitably, it shifted its definition of function and added a new, perhaps even visionary goal— to increase world food production. Achieving that goal of increased world food production it came to see as its new, narrowly defined, yet greatly expanding function.

While others in the fertilizer and allied agricultural industries struggled with the paradox, IMC began reshaping its corporate goals and the manner in which it served its customers. It was an important first step.

About this time, IMC's clientele in various parts of the world, including the Asia-Pacific region, North America, and parts of Europe and Latin America urgently began to suggest that help was needed in properly training their salesmen to take the fertilizer story more effectively and fully, more soundly and knowledgeably, to the farmers of the world.

As a result, IMC started a series of sales training sessions, sending its people out to train salesmen employed by its customers. During the first six to seven years of this effort, more than 5,000 sales people around the globe came to know the real purpose and value of fertilizer, and good fertilizer practices. They learned to know sound recommendations, to avoid overselling, and to sell the ultimate reward—greater yields, more productivity and improved crop quality.

So sure was IMC about the success of its sales training programs from the beginning, it became a subject of concern. Because if the production people in the plants run by its customers were not really producing high quality product capable of doing the job that was needed—and was being promised—then IMC's progress toward its goal would falter.

So, IMC added a series of training sessions for production people employed by its customers. Within a very few years, more than 4,000 of these people learned what they needed to know to back up *their* salesmen with high-quality product.

But then these newly-trained sales and production people began asking, "What is the value of training us if the people who run our business don't appreciate the principles and fundamentals that we learned in the training sessions?"

So, still several years before IMC undertook sponsorship of the World Food Production Conference, it began a management seminar (which it continues to hold each year) at its corporate headquarters. These seminars cover every phase of managing a business, including decision making, investment, finance, marketing, personnel development and training, and use all of the most advanced techniques, such as computerized decision-making, the games theory, and other advanced concepts of management. Those who attend are exposed to the instruments, the equipment, and the ideas that can help them become better managers of their respective businesses. Nearly one thousand owners and managers of customer companies around the world have benefitted from this program so far.

THE CORPORATE MOLECULE:

All of this reaching out by a raw materials supplier into the entire network of what, a few years earlier, it had not considered its proper responsibility, was beginning to have an effect at IMC. Each new piece of understanding, that came with each new entry into another link in the chain that put its product back into the earth, began to make the corporate molecule change. It now had to re-form itself toward a sense of future it had not previously anticipated, but could not—in the face of the evidence—deny.

For the reality in which the corporation functioned was changing. New information was being received all the time—information that forced IMC to acknowledge that to protect its destiny in this new reality it would have to further review its components, its direction, and its thrust.

Most of the new information was dire. In general terms, the Malthusian shadow was beginning to cast an eclipse-like darkness over much of the earth. Population was growing at a much faster rate than ever before and clearly outstripping agricultural gains. There was more hunger than there was food to quiet it. And the cries of children in far distant places could now be heard across the oceans, in the countries where there was still more food than hunger. The electronic magic of carrying sound pictures of newsworthy stories from around the globe brought the plight of people and the proportions of the Malthusian shadow into the speaking concern of nearly everyone.

A broader look at the situation told IMC that the world population would continue to increase faster than the production of food. It became clear that unless man did something about it, the hunger problem might have a destructive potential greater than that of a nuclear disaster, because hunger makes people irrational.

"We do not," said an IMC spokesman, "find rebellion and revolution in the world because people want television sets, but we do because they want food!" In France, the lack of food following the lean harvest of 1788 was high among the moving causes of the Great Revolution of 1789. Food is the first basic requirement and requisite for the survival of man. The need for an immediate increase in food production was the only solution apparent.

Apparent because of the startling fact that only 3% of the earth surface is arable. Just 3% of the earth's surface can grow food. Seventy percent is salt water and ice, desert, untillable rock, and swamp. And even if all the wonderful programs of irrigation, reclamation, and draining to improve and increase the available acreage were to prove successful, it is doubtful that it would ever reach a point where as much as 5% of the earth could be brought under food production of some kind.

Since it is only on the arable land that man's most basic need can be met, it follows that this land is his most precious asset. More precious by far than diamonds, emeralds or gold . . . nothing holds the secret of man's survival on earth more than that land. If it could be made to yield the most food possible— by improving the yield of every acre, everywhere—the shadow of Malthus could be erased.

With this underlying reasoning, IMC felt a new responsibility. It was not enough to consider only the simple equation that:

THE WORLD'S GREATEST PROBLEM IS HUNGER

THE WORLD'S GREATEST NEED IS FOOD

Now IMC saw a new factor, which, in its mind, amended that postulate to include the limited arable land question. This was the test of Malthus, for the people of the world had expanded and filled it out. There was no more land, for all practical purposes, but there were increasingly more people. Always more people, and never again more land. Therefore, IMC felt, the amended postulate should be stated:

THE WORLD'S GREATEST PROBLEM IS HUNGER

. . . AND THE WORLD'S GREATEST NEED IS

INCREASED FOOD PRODUCTION

Its full realization that the situation of the world and its food supply was correctly perceived galvanized the thinking at IMC. It was as if this realization functioned as a catalyst for the re-shaping of its corporate molecule. Then, IMC began to bend its full force toward a new and exciting corporate goal.

It had perceived its new corporate goal, within an industry goal and within a universal goal, and saw its responsibility clearly. Its new goal was to devote its full energies toward increasing the production of food. It saw, in abstracting this new corporate goal, that everything lined up perfectly; it foresaw both economic and social benefits. It seemed very pragmatic in character, and its proportions looked manageable. This objective made the kind of sense that could be defended before both stockholders or the United Nations. Its truth would stand up while the hunger problem was acute, and longer after it had ended. The realization was there that IMC had a significant role to play in alleviating the world's hunger problem. It knew that it dealt on only a narrow segment of that problem, but that it had the resources, the intellect, the application, the inclination, and the proclivities for producing the most food that can possibly be produced under existing conditions.

However, it knew that hunger won't wait. IMC management realized that by the time the problem was fully fathomed outside the field of agriculture and the planners, philosophers, politicians and public could begin talking about solving the problem in its totality—while this precious time was fleeting, hundreds of thousands would keep on dying of starvation.

IMC saw that, in the short run, the amount of food that can be produced under existing conditions is the only prerequisite for providing much moderation of the immediate problem. More food—increased food production—was the only answer. And IMC was sensitive enough to realize at the time that this was its line of work . . . that it was directly associated with the world hunger problem since it was important in the single most important variable for maximizing production at that time and under the state of the art that then existed. The corporate molecule had, in the heat generated by that realization, reformed itself into a new sense of responsibility. And once that occurred, amazing things began to happen.

the problem
suggests the solution

If more food was the need, and existing arable land the limitation, then it seemed only simple logic that the answer must be found by increasing the food yielding power of existing land. In modern terms that means the intensification of farming, by the employment of better farming methods.

That seems obvious to those in agriculture in the West. Experience gives ample evidence that the use of fertilizer, modern farm machinery, improved strains of seed, and irrigation, for example, produces more food. Within that general boundary of logic lay the answer; IMC was sure of it. And there were already strong indications that, with time and effort, those now basic concepts and practices could be adapted to the needs of the food-hungry nations. Some underdeveloped nations, with agronomic team assistance, have been known to leapfrog 100 years in a decade.

In Mexico, for example, wheat farmers in 1950 were producing only 11 bushels an acre. By 1958 their yield was up 118 percent to 24 bushels, and at the time IMC was pondering its future course, the yield had increased to over 40 bushels per acre with the best farmers harvesting 75 and 90 bushels. It could be done. In 1950, Mexico was importing 400,000 tons of wheat. By 1956 it was self-sustaining.

Until 1955, every tractor used in Brazil had to be imported. That year, domestic production of tractors was begun, and 53 units were produced. By 1964, the assembly lines were rolling out 33,000 tractors a year.

And scientists at the International Rice Research Institute near Manila were consistently producing, with new strains, 15 tons of rice per hectare; this compared with an average yield in the Philippines of just over one ton per hectare.

There were signs of great movement and activity, shaping up for combat with the great pressing concerns. Much of what was happening was already underway, though much of it required long periods of developmental time. Some time-shortening was becoming available from computer farming techniques just then being developed at IMC. To the question "What do computer routines have to do with world hunger?" the answer was that anything that promotes greater farm efficiency, promotes greater food production. General adoption and use of computer programs, IMC felt, could increase average yields in the U.S. cornbelt by 50 percent. In a somewhat longer time period the average yields could be doubled. The potential existed, it believed, to provide a 50 percent to 100 percent increase in food production in what was acknowledged to be one of the most modern agricultural systems in the world. All this just by adding the efficiencies of computer farming!

There were, IMC saw, great numbers of factors beginning to edge over the horizon of agriculture that held significant promise for the ultimate increase of food production.

It is known that farmers spend billions of dollars annually on fertilizers, tillage equipment, irrigation, weed control, and all the other elements of modern farming techniques. This is all done to improve the root environment of plants. Imagine the effect if that could be reversed—if *roots* could be changed to suit their environment.

There was the promise of a new agricultural sun, perhaps the sun of von Liebig, about to rise over the horizon. But the horizon was still some distance from where we stood. And hunger couldn't wait.

It was clear that science would eventually enable man to make new, different, unique plants, more ideally suited to the needs of the world. Indeed, it seemed that the ultimate limitation on agricultural progress would be only a lack of dynamic imagination. IMC summed it up with the estimate that "man has probably expended less than 5% of his mental capacities toward the growth of food around the world."

It was already apparent that 5 percent of man's intellect would not be sufficient to grow enough food for 100 percent of the world population on approximately 3 percent of the earth's surface.

IMC understood, through its examination of the problem, that the one constant element involved in all developments leading to increased food production was fertilizer. It was an integral part of every advance. Irrigation, for example, greatly enhances the use of fertilization, because more and more of the nutrients in the soil become available to the crops.

Similarly, the new strains of rice and wheat that were beginning to revolutionize agriculture with their startling yields, were drawing more heavily on the soil nutrients than ever before, and required more intensive fertilization. And the expanded use of modern farm machinery required the kind of investment that had to be backed up with crop reliability of the kind whose yield is based on fertilizer. Food and water are as basic to the sustenance of plants as they are to humans.

It was clear that intensified farming held the theoretical answer to the problem. The capability existed, inherently, to draw food from the earth in much greater quantities than ever before. And fertilizer was a prime requirement.

At the time, 1964, there were very few in the public eye who viewed the future with hope. A Malthusian crust seemed to have formed on public communication about hunger. Abrasive fears and doubts were raised, the long dark shadow of population being foremost among them. The intellectual outcry almost seemed shaped as an irrational, petulant, and adolescent outpouring of facts, figures and progressions, for which were claimed

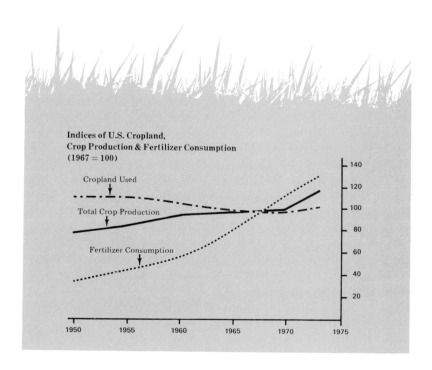

Indices of U.S. Cropland, Crop Production & Fertilizer Consumption (1967 = 100)

powers of clairvoyance offering a "true" look at the future. At the very least, it proved inertia-provoking in its self-fulfilling prophecy of helplessness.

IMC, industriously proceeding in the development of its philosophy, felt called upon to do something to reverse the trend of inaction. In preparation, it, too, looked toward the future . . .

LOOKING TOWARD THE FUTURE

IMC's look ahead was predicated on an understanding of where it stood. Every potential means of intensifying farming to increase food production seemed to involve the use of fertilizer. This would doubtless mean an increased demand as these methods were implemented.

Fertilizer was a product that, by itself, could substantially increase food production. Even if it took time to develop and distribute, and to educate farmers in other modern farming methods, fertilizer could help both immediately and in the future.

Fertilizer, IMC knew, could help alone, and nothing else could help much without it. It was both basic and immediate, and not only was the cost of implementing its use much lower than the introduction of other improvements, it almost invariably returned its cost several times over when the harvest went to market.

Viewed this way, the future looked brighter than ever. Shipping fertilizer was much more practical in both dollars and sense than shipping food. One ship load of fertilizer would result in ten times the food production that could have been shipped in the same vessel. Likewise, its cost was a fraction of the cost of harvested grain.

Even more importantly for the less developed countries, its use involved the simplest education of all modern farming methods, it was easiest to supply, and it did not impinge on traditional farming practices or require mechanization to any appreciable degree. The record of fertilization alone, in the increase of food, was amazing.

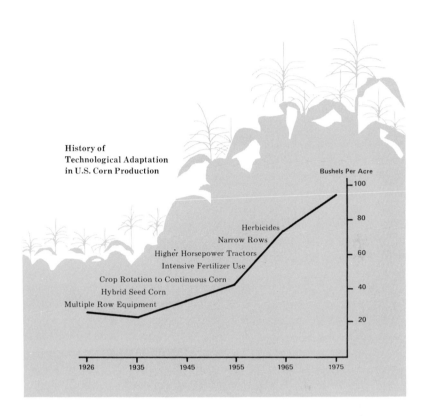

History of
Technological Adaptation
in U.S. Corn Production

Bushels Per Acre

Herbicides
Narrow Rows
Higher Horsepower Tractors
Intensive Fertilizer Use
Crop Rotation to Continuous Corn
Hybrid Seed Corn
Multiple Row Equipment

100
80
60
40
20

1926   1935   1945   1955   1965   1975

PROBLEMS IN THE FUTURE OF FERTILIZER

All of which is not to say that IMC did not find problems that needed to be computed in its forecast of the future. It did.

In 1962 fertilizer consumption, worldwide, was 30 million metric tons. Two short years later it had risen to 36.6 million tons, indicating a new rate of annual growth of more than 10 percent, a figure unprecedented in history.

Projecting towards 1980, the statistics became alarming when viewed through the eyes of responsible businessmen. Population projections indicated that by 1980 the growth factor alone would require the application of an additional 20 million tons of fertilizer per year if food needs were to even remain at the same unhappy level.

But the world does not stand still, and increased standards

of living were already manifesting themselves in terms of increased meat consumption. It takes, on the average, five grams of grain to produce one gram of meat. If these projected needs were to be met, an additional 13 million tons of fertilizer would be needed every year.

Beyond both of these, IMC reasoned, we must replace the nutrients which are drained from the soil. To do that would mean another additional 15 million tons. Increasing farm capitalization, largely in the U.S. and other developed nations, would create a new market for 20 million tons. And government action, expanding technology, and a variety of other factors would probably account for still another 15 million tons.

Adding it up, the total world requirement for fertilizer in 1980 was seen to be 113 million tons a year, if all needs were to be met.

Interestingly, the population increase projected for that period was 37 percent, which would bring the world to four-and-a-half billion people by 1980. But in that same period, the world need for fertilizer would jump 250 percent to 113 million tons!

Ordinarily, the expectation of good business prospects ahead is not alarming to a private sector corporation. But this, for IMC, had a frightening aspect. For this was much more than a matter of business; this was what was going to be needed to grow food for the world.

The total world facilities for the production of fertilizer represented an investment approximating $3 billion. Production capacity was 38 million tons. Planned construction would raise that to 56 million tons. To meet the projected 1980 need of 113 million tons would require the additional investment of $11 billion. No one could even guess where that might come from.

In beginning to think about meeting the world's needs for the short term future, it was clear to IMC management that the problems needed a lot of talking about. Much planning would be needed to deal with the world's needs if, in just this one small area of concern alone, the projections could turn up problems of such enormity. Clearly it was necessary to begin to focus concern on the future.

The logic of this situation suggested to IMC that if the world fertilizer suppliers began focusing their attention on the problem, the inescapable first step would have been taken. There could then be a forum dealing with world food production, looking at both current pressing needs, and those promising to be even more urgent in the future. Of all the agricultural advances, fertilizer seemed to emerge as the most immediately available, lowest cost and most practical tool for increasing the nutrient-yielding efficiency of the land. It was time to make the industry—and the world of need—aware of how it might figure in the fight against hunger.

IMC realized that neither it—nor the entire industry it was part of—had the capability to resolve the problem of world hunger; but it further reasoned that nothing meaningful could be done without it. IMC suspected that the fertilizer suppliers who were its customers would be in the best position to further immediate improvement in the world's supply of food. At least it was a place to start.

At this point the structure of the new corporate molecule completed its transformation. The philosophy of IMC had firmed. To implement that philosophy, it made plans to call together its customers and others. Thus was the first World Food Production Conference conceived.

Invitations were sent to those who IMC knew had a dedicated interest in raising the universal consciousness of need, and who could raise their industry sights above sales and profits to focus on the broader goals of increasing world food production.

Because hunger can't wait, the situation seeemed clear, the logic seemed undeniable, and the responsibility was deeply felt. IMC had made its commitment.

the first world food production conferences take form

Planning for the first World Food Production Conference was intense. The stakes were high and the route uncharted. Such a conference had to do more than produce talk. There would need to be discussion, of course, but only discussion that could ultimately lead to action. Hunger was widespread and growing, so the focus on increased food production needed to be sharpened in terms of social responsibility. Still, IMC realized, this couldn't realistically be done at the expense of business responsibility. Unifying these two goals was seen as vital to success, both for the conference and for the increased availability of food.

Recognizing that man, now in the 20th century, must feed himself where he stood, because there was no further significant land expansion option open to him, it was important that those in agriculture knew with exactness where they stood. They must know what actually exists, what could be expected, and how to bring the knowledge and expertise of the world's agronomists together constructively. Patterns for progress had to be determined, so that obstacles—as they were identified— could be removed, and the science and skills of the modern world put into a single encompassing harness pulling toward a single goal. No matter what else happened, IMC believed, it was important that the major production forces of the world be aimed in a unified direction, toward an elemental goal. And that goal had to be the end of human hunger. The job of agriculture was to provide enough food to end the nightmare spectre of worldwide starvation.

Behind it all was the belief that it could be done. The purpose of the conference had to be—in its largest sense—to do it! At least, to make a beginning by convincing others that it could be done. This meant disseminating the knowledge that existed to farmers everywhere, and to all those industries, government agencies, and others whose commercial or scientific interests had a role to play in agriculture.

The challenge, obviously, was enormous. Breathtaking, in fact. Viewed in terms of the limited capacity of one corporation it seemed impossible! But, it *was* possible to start . . . to make a beginning.

To do so, the overall problem needed first to be broken down into manageable problems, and then attacked one by one. IMC realized that, in the face of the compound, complex dimensions of world hunger, any corporation that tried to associate itself with the total problem could only endanger its credibility. Hunger had been growing year by year and was gaining in momentum. To make a grandstand play of attacking it whole could fast become a joke or, at best, lock that corporation into an indefensible and impossible situation.

So the planning was restricted to an approach of relevancy. IMC would organize the conference around its own background of success. It had increased the awareness of its own personnel— some 10,000 of them around the world—and been successful. It had made them aware not only of the importance of their work in food production, but inspired them to seek the distant goal of food sufficiency for the world. It knew well the ground on which it stood.

The first step in planning, therefore, was to set a specific, though unspoken, goal for the conference. The place to start was obvious. The conference would be designed to add as much as possible to the considerable abilities of the conferees who were already in positions of responsibility, with both the resources and the desire to serve the people of their countries.

It was decided not to hold the conference in one of the publicity centers of the western world, where exposure to the media would be greatest, instead it would be deep within an area of great need. It was decided that the way to begin (and provide a convincing basis for credibility) was to provide a meeting that would inspire and motivate the conferees to want to bring home as quickly as possible the ideas they had been exposed to—from one another and from IMC—for growing more food for their own market. The conference, then, would not so much deal in world hunger, as in local needs. World hunger, it was seen, was only a motivating concept, but hungry people were a fact. It would be this fact, in local terms, that would underlie the conference.

The meetings, therefore, were projected as pragmatic and practical. Not as a forum for the debate of philosophies, but as an opportune expedient where ideas might be spun like silk and woven into the fabric of the mind in such a manner that they could be taken home and unravelled into pragmatic progress.

Information, not demagoguery, was what was wanted. For example, at an early conference, the fact that one week's difference in planting time can affect a crop yield by as much as 25 percent, became known. This single fact is of immense and immediate value in areas of the world where a high proportion of inhabitants do not have enough to eat. That kind of knowledge can immediately translate into more food with the next growing season.

It was hoped the World Food Production Conference could create an atmosphere of broad, mutual understanding, reaching across boundaries of both land and mind, with concern for the feeding of people, and be helpful in increasing the means to that accomplishment.

That was the way it began.

When the first World Food Production Conference assembled in Hong Kong ten years ago, all the conferees had strong relationships to the fertilizer industry. They brought their own credibility with them because if everything else was held constant, the incremental value of fertilizer exceeds the incremental value of all other inputs in the process of producing food. Fertilizer is the single most important variable for maximizing the production of food.

So, while recognizing that there are many facets to the problem of world hunger, IMC's only credible participation--as with most of those assembled—was in one very narrow segment of the overall food problem. Together, those assembled had the resources, the intellect, the application, the inclination, and the proclivities for producing the most food possible in their areas under the existing conditions of that day. These were fertilizer people, present and ready to begin a concerted battle on the food problems of their time.

But it wasn't that simple. There were peripheral problems. These began to emerge at the conference. More, it seemed, stood between fertilizer and the farmer than an understanding of von Liebig's principles of soil enrichment.

Japan, for example, is one of the world's largest users of chemical fertilizers. Its rate of application is among the highest anywhere, running to 356 lbs. per acre. Japan has reason to believe in fertilizer benefits and has engaged substantial sums of capital to create facilities for its manufacture. Much of what is produced is offered for foreign exchange.

It was a representative of one of the major industrial enterprises in Japan, who pinpointed a specific problem:

> "... *Southeast Asia has approximately half the population of the world, with a rapid rate of population increase. Certainly this area has a great potential for increasing food production by using more fertilizers. But, things are not so easy and simple. They have no money to buy fertilizers. Unless we can help them to earn money, the great potential will remain as potential and never become an actual demand. Here, Japan can play an important role. Japan is in a position to help them make money by improving trade with them* ..."

> ... *from conference proceedings, 1965*

He then outlined Japan's needs for many imports and its desire to exchange fertilizer for them in foreign trade. He explained that, for a variety of reasons, including political problems, these exchanges do not always materialize. He told, for example, of piles of fertilizers shipped from Japan left on the wharves of Indonesia instead of being transferred to the farmyards simply because there was no effective transportation and distribution organization. Which seems a tragedy in itself, but then he got to the heart of the matter:

> "On the other hand," *he asked,* "are farmers anxious for fertilizers? I don't think so. What does it gain these young farmers to work hard to produce more food than they themselves need? The excess food they produce is taken by the government at a cheap official price and they have to pay high, black market prices to buy daily necessities.*
>
> *"Productivity would seem to be a goal which does not pay. So resolution of this complex problem cannot be reached only by economic measures. We have to approach the question politically, though even that is not enough. Equally important, I assert, is education. This may appear to be a roundabout way, but I think it is the surest means of solving the matter. Of course, educating farm-*

ers on how to use fertilizer and pesticides is important. But education for all the people in what democracy is, and what a prosperous economy is—one that gives the people a comfortable, healthy living— is equally important.

"To turn the potentials of more fertilizers and more food production into actuality, education is the most important key to opening up this new phase. The developed countries should use more of their aid money for education and the fight against illiteracy. So I assert that, to solve freedom from hunger, freedom from ignorance is most important. Unless we try hard to find an educational approach, the greatest potential will remain always potential, I am afraid."

. . . from conference proceedings, 1965

Quickly it began to emerge and become clear to those present that it was going to be difficult, if not impossible, to limit the conference focus to even so basic an element of agriculture as fertilizer. Fertilizer did not stand alone in the world of reality as a viable means of combating hunger, but rather was inextricably involved with other social forces, including economics, politics and education. No matter how obvious and singular the value of fertilizer had seemed in theory, there were places where it was held in suspension by other tangled forces that would need to be unknotted, in order to free it to do its work.

A similar expression of the constraints surrounding immediate increases in fertilizer use in order to affect food production within a single growing season was voiced by a conferee representing the management of a massive new fertilizer manufacturing complex in the Philippines. He, too, addressed himself to farmer motivation:

"One of the problems in the Philippines, too, is that the farmer often has little incentive to grow more than he is growing at the present time. The government does not guarantee a flow of price that would make his productivity economic, so that where it would be possible in many parts of the Philippines to get two and three crops with adequate irrigation, the farmer grows only one. Three-fourths of all rice grown in the Philippines is used for personal subsistence, and only about a fourth of it goes to market. This situation

will never be overcome if the farmer has no economic incentive to get a decent price for his rice.

"When fertilizer was experimentally subsidized to rice and corn growers, 52,000 tons went through the hands of a government agency. Of that amount, only 27,000 tons ever got on the rice and corn crops; the remainder was black marketed to the sugar industry which could pay more for it. Therefore, I consider the statement on political implications in varying degrees affecting the use of fertilizer to be among the most important."

. . . from conference proceedings, 1965

The shadow of politics falling over food is, at first, a disturbing consideration. Man's imperfections in social organization are always a factor and where incentives to steal outweigh those to work, special problems are obviously induced.

But among the components that established the basic spine of conference intent was the strong belief that there was no point in meeting if the conferees did not meet in frankness and honesty, speaking freely of everything necessary to understand not only the means of increasing the production of food, but also of the impediments to it. Insofar as this related to action, however, the *a priori* determination was not to get sidetracked.

Conference action would be taken in the areas of production, not politics. Politics would certainly be recognized, as it is everywhere, as a reality that must be accepted. But, except for developing a concrete understanding of the ways in which it impinged on food production, there seemed no surer way to bog down meaningful conference activity than to take it into the political arena. IMC had, in its root philosophy from which the conference merged, a sense of conviction that promised to work with people everywhere. It was determined to help whomever has fertilizer resources in their country, be it private or government enterprise. It was the reality of food production for hungry humans, that IMC meant to affect, and that reality was just as important in one political entity as in another. Observed another participant:

"With respect to land reform (in Venezuela) we have been able to carry out a program which, during the first five years, gave 80,000

families their own land. These people are already beginning to realize the advantages of fertilizers, and are beginning to use them in a very profitable manner.

"In this way Venezuela has been able to overcome one of the most difficult problems developing countries have. It has been stated that a dynamic land reform would cause damaging repercussions in the production of food. In Venezuela, it has been possible to show that, not only has dynamic land reform been carried out, but we also have avoided the decline in food production that so often follows.

"As a matter of fact, Venezuelan production and productivity as a whole has shown a spectacular increase between 1945 and 1960, with a growth ratio of 6 percent during the last five years. This growth ratio from the moment the land reform was launched has increased at a yearly cumulative rate of 8 percent - 9 percent. We can say that this is an example, in spite of many errors, of a successful land reform program. It presents positive evidence it can be done and, at the same time, increase agricultural productivity."

. . . from conference proceedings, 1965

From the outset the conference response was generally interpreted as providing information, not about politics, but about the potential that existed for the improvement of yield. The conferees were discussing, by implication, the potential in some areas for increasing crops as much as 300 percent by means of improved irrigation and fertilizing techniques and, in other areas, by land reform. This gradual unfolding of bits and pieces of information about potential confirmed the optimism that underlay the establishment of the conference.

One of the major values of the first World Food Production Conference was that it immediately provided a forum for the introduction of the human complex that had yet to be penetrated in order to get results.

The level at which these men were meeting was established early. Being the first of its kind, this conference did not know if it could hope to accomplish much more than develop an understanding of the real problem, exchange honest and helpful information and, perhaps, establish practical channels through which the identification of problems might pass—hopefully, toward a means that could begin to lessen them. It was the future that was important, and planning for the future began to be evident at the very first meeting, when another conferee from Japan spoke up:

> *"I think it might be useful to set up an agricultural bank that would enable us to try a triangular trade. Don't you agree that it would be advantageous if we could establish an agricultural bank and pool all rice produced in Korea, Taiwan and Japan, and sell it to those countries in southeast Asia that have shortages?*
>
> *"This is just an example of one commodity—rice. Rice that can be produced in southeast Asia very easily without much, or often without any, fertilizer at all. As a result, unless farmers can sell this rice by means of pooling, controlled by an organization such as an agricultural bank, there will be great difficulties that could, if they were to become extreme, result in a price war among the farmers.*
>
> *"If such a bank were to be successful with rice, it could also be employed by many other agricultural products."*

> *. . . from conference proceedings, 1965*

It was profound practicalities such as this that the conference was seeking. Ideas that had practical promise. Ideas that could work through the web of complexity, knotted at every turn by social or economic or political kinks that obstructed both an increase in the growth of food, and its delivery to the market. Clearly, it was man, not nature, who stood between himself and an adequate food supply. Knowledge already existed that could spring a harvest of bounty several times greater than any we have ever known from the land that lies between the poles of the earth. But how to urge man to bring it forth?

Here was a suggestion that could skillfully untie one of the myriad of small knots that needed to be loosened before the food production maze could be untangled. It was a place to start, and conference chairman A. E. Cascino, of IMC, responded to it gladly:

> *"We will record officially, as a part of this conference, the suggestion that the world give thought to establishing a food bank. If not on a*

worldwide basis, on a sectional or regional basis, wherein the food surplus producing nations would somehow find a way to economically contribute to the food bank and then this food bank would find a way to equitably distribute it among the food deficient nations of that section or region. I think this is a very important and original idea, and I congratulate the speaker for having made this such an important contribution of the conference itself."

. . . from conference proceedings, 1965

The immediate response of IMC to the first World Food Production Conference it sponsored was positive in the extreme. The gamble for credibility had been immediately resolved. Moreover, the corporation saw that it had never really been in question. The conferees had worked with great sincerity, as is obvious. Their seriousness of purpose was evident from the start. Discussion was honest and forthright, and aimed directly at the target—hunger. The production of more food, together with the impediments to that, had been the problems put before them. The conferees had responded at the high level of responsibility asked of them, and were eager to continue their participation.

"I'm sure it will be the unanimous opinion of the group that the subjects presented have been so important that all we ask now is how we can move forward in our own areas to give the kind of service and advanced thinking to agriculture that IMC does. Second, I think it would be a good thing to schedule meetings like this every year, or every two years, in order that we can exchange points of view and experiences . . ."

. . . from conference proceedings, 1965

". . . the Conference has brought many ideas to our minds. I think that in Mexico there are several areas where the ideas and thoughts expressed in this conference could be implemented. This will start us moving on the way we have ahead of us . . ."

. . . from conference proceedings, 1965

"To my mind this meeting we have held here in this beautiful city of Caracas, the pictures we have seen, the discussions that have taken place, and the papers presented reflect the dynamic management of IMC. I believe all these events are the natural result of the excellent work carried out by this dynamic management. I do not question for one minute that this philosophy, which these gentlemen have not only created, but have also put into practice, will be very successful and will be used by us, for example, in our own factories."

. . . from conference proceedings, 1965

". . . I consider the many ideas shown here to be very valuable and I, also, am considering their probable implementation when I get back to my own country . . ."

. . . from conference proceedings, 1965

". . . These discussions have been very helpful since they have allowed me to obtain a good idea about the situation prevailing in the agriculture of other countries. On the other hand, I must confess that, in spite of the many publications I have read, I had no idea of the long way we still have ahead in this field."

. . . from conference proceedings, 1965

"I want to say that this panel has been so interesting and so useful for us that it is practically our duty to help IMC in all ways we can. Therefore, as speaker on behalf of my firm, I would assure you that we will go [to the site of any future conference] and only a catastrophe could prevent us from doing so."

. . . from conference proceedings, 1965

IMC, too, found the conference credible and pragmatic. As it had wanted. As it had planned. All discussion seemed to easily interweave a justifiable economic base with a justifiable base of social responsibility. It was now proved, what had before been only conceived—that profitable business and fulfillment of social needs need not be conflicting. This was a critically important ingredient in the fully-developed corporate philosophy, and it was important that it prove itself in the heat of conference fire.

For, as much as anything, IMC hoped the conference would spark other corporations into new activity of a roughly similar nature in which humanitarian and business interests could be merged. It felt that a new era of corporate responsibility was necessary. IMC felt it was imperative that it begin to happen, and wanted to achieve with the conference an indication of what could be accomplished by a single corporate entity by bringing these two apparently polar interests into focus.

That the world must be fed was a given fact. The practical means of accomplishing that end were of as much self-importance to the health of business interests in agriculture and commercially allied fields as they were to the hungry people of the world. It involved not the same interests, perhaps, but certainly overlapping interests that were capable of mutual benefit. IMC, having looked, had found such an area of overlapping interest. It was hopeful that by demonstrating this forcefully with these conferences it might encourage others to look toward the goal of feeding the hungry. It hoped others would see that addressing this task would lead to significant gains, not only in the welfare of the world's people, but for the business interests who had to provide the conduits through which increased food production must pass.

With the seeds of interest and concern firmly planted, IMC then undertook the ongoing responsibility for their nourishment. It made the commitment to continue sponsorship of the World Food Production Conference on a regular annual basis.

conference content
...an overview

It was important that the early conferences develop a means of getting deeply into the hunger problem, much the same way a tick burrows underneath the skin and makes something happen right away. Theory was not enough. It was never going to be enough merely to take a survey of human hunger. The first conferences could be compared to establishing a clinic. People came and talked about what was wrong, with an abiding personal interest in finding some way to make it stop hurting. The conference intent was to be pragmatic, but first—as in a clinic—it was necessary to know and understand the background and circumstance of its history.

One task accomplished by the early conferences was to point up the scope and dimension of the real-world problem. In effect, these turned on the lights so conferees could actually see what had happened to prevent some country that had a demonstrated *need* for fertilizer from buying it and using it. They had to know *why not*, to help devise means of overcoming the problem.

So the early conferences were aimed directly at opening up the wells of discontent. They strove to bring forward the full range of problems as they were perceived by the conferees representing agricultural interests in the underdeveloped nations, those food-insufficient nations which were the homes of hunger and world nutrition.

For everywhere hunger seemed to be the iron hook at the end of a long line of economic and other factors. In some places, answers had been found. These were discussed, in the hope that others present might see how such an answer might work—with local variations—in their own countries.

For example, the following exchange took place:

> CHAIRMAN: (to conferee) You introduced a new thought here which I think is one the agriculture industry around the world must give serious consideration to. That is the need to introduce

*new products to agriculture that have more worldwide appeal.
So many of our agricultural economies are based on producing
a series of products that fit the unique requirements of the country in which they are contained. But agriculture, if it is going to
produce food for the world, must produce food palatable and
desirable for other countries. I notice you spoke of rice and sugar
cane as Taiwan's major products though in recent years you have
introduced pineapple, bananas and mushrooms. How important
are they in your economy?*

*CONFEREE: Well, in recent years we have exported lots of bananas
to our trade. Quite a big amount. The mushroom is quite a new
crop. We export to Europe, to the United States, and to Japan.
There is no conflict with rice and sugar production because
most of our bananas are planted on slopes and mountain areas
which cannot be cultivated for rice and sugar cane. The mushrooms occupy a very small area, but in the amount of foreign
exchange, they help us a great deal.*

*CHAIRMAN: I think this is a very interesting twist. Here you have
gone to land that is marginal, sides of hills, and so on, to produce
products that don't interrupt the basic products but are more
highly exportable, command a pretty good price in the market,
and, therefore, help you in the foreign exchange market. Very,
very well done . . ."*

. . . from conference proceedings, 1965

The early conferences were deeply imbued with the urgency of
hunger. Such information as that from Taiwan was important.
It was something that had been done, and had been successful.

Just as gladly received, though not yet proved, were a whole
spate of ideas and plans that were "in the works" at one or
another stage of development. It was important to include
them, to let the conferees know about things that were about
to happen, as well as things that were happening or had already
happened.

The varied topics revolved dizzily around the wheel of progress, accomplished or intended. Knowing that something was
happening—or was about to somewhere—could give impetus to
something that one's own country wanted, for which the full
data was not yet assembled, or where the full confidence of

the agencies required to make it happen had not yet been achieved. An early expression of what later became a very big story, indeed, first came forward in skeletal form:

> *"The Philippines, as you know, is a net importer of rice. In the year 1965, it spent $65 million of foreign exchange importing rice. The Philippines could be a net exporter of rice and, indications are, with the active participation of the government, three bodies will help achieve this self-sufficiency of rice within the next three years. These three are the International Rice Research Institute, the U.S. AID program, and private industry.*
>
> *"President Marcos has gone to great lengths to provide the right atmosphere. He is attempting to do something about the infrastructure. Last week, there was a national congress of the Catholic Church to endeavor to interest them in improving the lot of the poorer farmer. Now I think what this is all leading up to is that the country will be self-sufficient in rice probably within three years, and in five years can be a net exporter. . . ."*
>
> *. . . from conference proceedings, 1967*

Ideas shot out of the early conferences like spokes radiating from a central hub. If a rim could have been attached around the spokes it would probably have encircled the basic area of hunger, and provided a comprehensive map of the territory that had to be covered to vanquish the problem. It was the wheel of worldwide concern that was forming. Once formed, it could, hopefully, be made to roll.

At its hub, at the very center of all the expressed ideas, stood fertilizer. Those assembled knew the value of fertilizers. But each knew mainly in terms of the industry components with which he was most familiar. This was long before worldwide attention had been drawn to the need for increased food production, and before the full subject had become a common currency spent largely by the loose tongues of those with ready access to publicity. Here, in the early days of the World Food Production Conferences, there was no common currency. There was only common need and uncommon concern.

In his address to the very first conference at Hong Kong, the guest speaker—a man who was Professor of Economics at the

University of Hong Kong, who had a lifelong interest in agro-
nomics, who had been born in Japan and lived most of his life
in Southeast Asia, though educated in both the United States
and England—firmly established the center of food production
concern. He spoke of the hub from a different point of view:

> *"Man is playing a losing game against nature, so far. But, we have a
> trump card, and certainly the trump card which might turn this
> game might be fertilizers. On the social and political sides, also, the
> cards are stacked against us in the underdeveloped countries. The
> agrarian systems are backward and inefficient. There are systems
> and institutions which are oppressive and limiting and these are
> firmly rooted, especially in the countryside, even more than in the
> towns. There is ignorance. There is lack of incentive and lack of
> initiative which must be overcome.*
>
> *"During the remainder of the 20 Century, according to the U.N.
> projections, and these are the median U.N. projections, not the
> highest or the lowest, it is expected that the population in the under-
> developed countries may increase by nearly three billion, while the
> population in the developed countries increases by 0.4 billion. So,
> at present, there are approximately three people in the underdevel-
> oped, poor countries for each person in the well-developed coun-
> tries. By the year 2000, this ratio may change to 5 to 1 at best.*
>
> *"The output of grain per capita, because of the big increase of
> population in the underdeveloped countries, has actually fallen by
> 3 percent in the last 30 years. In the next 30 years the people of
> the underdeveloped countries will have to practically double produc-
> tion just to maintain their present unhappy, low levels; to bring
> them up near the rest of the world at all they must treble, or quad-
> ruple their production, or even more.*
>
> *"So, increasing the fertility of the soil is by far the most im-
> portant consideration before us. Fertilizers are essential. They must
> play a large, even heroic part in this battle."*
>
> *. . . from conference proceedings, 1965*

Among the early attempts to further open up thinking was a
comment that sought to break down any artificial barrier between theory and practice. While those present were very much
aware of the value of fertilizers, that meant little if that aware-

ness was not made broader in the realm of agriculture. The practical meaning of that concern was driven home forcefully by a conferee from the Philippines:

> "... *Our biggest problem is to persuade farmers to use fertilizer. Of all the farmers in the Philippines, only about 30 percent have ever used chemical fertilizers, while the remaining 70 percent do not use fertilizer at all. We found that the main reasons for this could be split into four basic headings: 1. Educational; 2. Economic or financial; 3. Social; and 4. Supply.*
>
> *"Under educational, 21 percent was based on lack of knowledge; 16 percent said the soil was still fertile so there was no need for fertilizer; and 17 percent had no experience.*
>
> *"Under economic or financial, 37 percent said it was lack of money or credit, while only 6 percent said it was high cost.*
>
> *"On the social side, 7 percent gave as a reason the unfair tenancy arrangement, another 3 percent lack of motivation.*
>
> *"Supply problems were given as a reason for non-use by 17 percent of the farmers.*
>
> *"The average farm holdings are small. Of all farms in the Philippines, 75 percent are less than 4 hectares; 43 percent are less than 2 hectares. The median size farm is 2.3 hectares.*
>
> *"And yet another factor is the relative youth of the Philippine population; 69 percent is under age 35, and 35 percent is under age 15. So this limits experience in the use of fertilizer. ...*"
>
> *... from conference proceedings, 1965*

The expression of such concerns as these for the widening gulf between the farmers in food-short areas and their comprehension of the potential value of fertilizer for improving the quality of their lives (as well as others) were, of course, countered by thoughts on how such farmers might be brought to see themselves as more closely allied to the need to fertilize. One ingeniously expressed thought in this regard sought to examine the farmer in a different light altogether:

> "... *What kind of business is the farmer really in? Basically, his business is the production of food and fiber. His products are essen-*

tially proteins, fats, cellulose and carbohydrates, all of which are processed chemicals, with the exception of seed. They are produced with nothing but chemical raw materials, therefore, we can only conclude that the farmer is running a chemical synthesis factory in his soil. Without realizing it, he, too, is in the chemical industry, just as we are . . ."

. . . from conference proceedings, 1966

Thoughts, ideas, and information were exchanged and travelled from one nation to another across the conference tables. Interest was uniformly intense, as the conferees had come well prepared with comments, ideas and conclusions:

". . . *Examination of the basic problems and alternatives leads me to the conclusion that there are certain basic principles which must be followed in seeking the optimum solution to the world's urgencies in agriculture. First, we must constantly seek to provide fertilizers and the other inputs that the farmer requires at the lowest possible cost. We must be sure that a total approach is taken at the farm level so that the farmer at all times has all the necessary requisites to produce higher yields of food.*

"Second, we must consider that there exists in the world today all of the necessary knowledge and experience required to elevate agricultural levels in the developing countries. The question becomes how to bridge this communication gap between those nations or companies that have the necessary knowledge, and those people in the developing countries who need this information. There is little doubt that through proper communication, correct education at the farm level can bring about a dramatic and rapid improvement in agricultural productivity if made available and if properly communicated.

"The third principle which we must consider is that the farmer will respond to raising his food production levels if, in addition to the raw material inputs and knowledge, he is provided with suitable credit to buy the necessary materials—and keep in mind that many farmers in the world have per capita incomes of less than one hundred dollars per year—while simultaneously being given adequate

incentives to make a profit and raise his standard of living in order
to keep the upward trend of increased production moving.

"This leads to the fourth point; that government, which, in the
final analysis, has normally manipulated the farmer for the benefit
of the nation as a whole, must provide the farmer with sufficient
incentives so that he is motivated to make a profit. It also means
that governments must work arm in arm with the business system
or companies providing the various inputs to the farmer. . . ."

. . . from conference proceedings, 1967

From every possible combination of factors, ideas came forth. The number of intricate local systems of activity, finance, and overall agricultural structure that revealed themselves were amazing. And yet, each viewpoint added greatly to the conference understanding of the complex barriers between man and his food supply.

Nothing meaningful about the subject can be said in a sentence. Something that could provide an answer for one nation does not necessarily have the capability of providing the answer for others. There seemed little difference of opinion about the broadest principles of agriculture, or the need for more food. But how one got from here to there was more than a question . . . it was a mass of questions. Of course, the basic representation at the earliest conferences was from the private sector. And the greatest concern logically revolved around how the private sector could be engaged in the struggle for more food. The conference did not try to mind other people's business, only its own.

However, the private sector does not operate in a social vacuum. And it does not operate, *cannot* operate, where there is a profit vacuum. It is designed to work effectively where, for something put in, there is something equitable to be gotten out. That was one of the realities it seemed important for the conference to accept. And the conference had little trouble doing so. This was a joint concern, a concern for food and future, and *future* meant staying in business to be able to continue the supply of food nutrients to nutrient-hungry land. That was the exchange it offered toward the goal of producing food for hungry people.

But the private sector is not capable of doing everything. This was clearly recognized by all present, and was particularly well summed up by one participant:

> "... Within this framework it will be necessary for the government to involve itself deeply. In the face of current Brazilian reality, only the government can accomplish all these things, whether it be contracting for a greater number of teachers, or furnishing more adequate and abundant teaching materials, or structuring a school curriculum which is more objective and practical. This governmental work implies an increase in the cost of public instruction, but it will be one of the most useful investments for the future of the country, with immediate effects on the development of our agriculture..."

>   ... from conference proceedings, 1966

Essentially, the early conferences were eager to put every instrumental agency of man into harness. Every available bit of power and strength that could be so harnessed was needed to get the food picture into proper perspective. Reality was the key thought in the proceedings. How *can* it be done, not how *should* it be done. The World Food Production Conference was aimed at heading off widespread starvation not only in the future, but in the immediate world surrounding the very meeting places of the conference. It was this sense of reality and need that lured a succession of busy men away from their priority concerns into an idea arena that promised them help from, and their help to, the others assembled.

Every resource that could be brought to bear on the problem was to be involved. The conference was not to be a place for judgment, but for ideas and action.

The catalyst for turning ideas into action is money. And here at the conference the private sector felt its limitations. It had money invested in every phase and facet of the fertilizer industry, and new capital investment demand was burdening the industry considerably. Plans were already underway for additional capital expansion to increase the ability of the industry to meet the expanding need for its product clearly seen ahead. Yet the concerns being voiced at the conference indicated an

equally clear need for considerable expenditure in other areas
of agriculture, if the ability of the world's farmers to increase
their yields was to be increased.

Other agencies of finance reported themselves present, and
willing and able to be of service:

> *"For us at the World Bank, the topic of this conference is most
> important, and it is the most exciting item on our own agenda . . .
> I want to share with you some of our impressions and attitudes with
> respect to our problems, and to communicate what we think are
> some of the lessons we have learned, and are learning, by our ac-
> tivities in promoting agricultural development . . .*
>
> *"Events in the past several years indicate that we have entered
> a period of transition, from traditional forms of food production to
> a modern agriculture dependent on cooperation between corpora-
> tions and industry, in the production and distribution of farm
> chemicals, machinery and equipment for the farmer and in the
> processing and marketing of farm outputs.*
>
> *"Even during the early phases of development, private enterprise
> provided much of the capital and initiative in opening up new lands.
> In the current phase of modernizing our agriculture, we expect
> private enterprise to play an even more crucial role. The World Bank
> has realized the importance of helping Latin America accomplish
> its present development growth. In the past two years we have lent,
> in Latin America, about $350 million a year. In the current year,
> we may reach a level slightly in excess of $500 million. By 1972,
> we expect to lend somewhere between $700 and $800 million a
> year . . .*
>
> *"In Latin America, which has a very high average rate of popula-
> tion growth, agricultural production has just managed to keep pace
> with the number of mouths it has to feed. However, as the economy
> grows, and incomes rise, the rural sector will be called upon to
> produce far more food and fiber than at present, and this increased
> effort will require more capital investment, both public and private,
> and a general improvement of the institutional framework within
> which farmers and agricultural industries now operate. The need
> for investment and increased productivity is brought home very
> clearly when one considers that by the end of the century the
> population of Latin America will have grown by about 400 million
> over present levels, and will be advancing, roughly, at a rate of 100
> million every five years. Our own objective is quite simple. It is to*

assist both large and small farmers in increasing their production substantially, and economically. We will lend for irrigation, for fertilizer plants, for agricultural extension services, for banks to provide farm credit, for the improvement of livestock and seed varieties, pesticide production, agricultural machinery, food processing and storage facilities. . . ."

. . . from conference proceedings, 1969

The tone of the conferences was set, essentially, during the early years. It took time, of course, to get all the problems on the table, and it took time to locate and define all the wide avenues of obstacles to the increased production of food.

Hunger, the root subject of the conference, was discussed in penetrating terms. However, as the evidence began to present itself, it became increasingly evident that not only were there known and existing means of advancing the nutrition levels of worldwide humanity, but that with the exchange of information about educational problems, financial problems, distribution problems, and so on, it *was* possible to conceive of it really happening. The early hopes had been proved even beyond expectation. The things that were keeping food from the collective mouth of humanity were *man* things, not *nature* things. They were the imperfections in the world's social development. It was where the paving ended on the roads to market, where the credit ended on the banking system, where the education stopped, and where real opportunities had been overlooked. It was a maze of problems, and learning of their nature and extent at the conference did not lessen the problem. But it did make one significant difference. It began to put bulls-eye targets up at the end of the range. Specific objectives became more visible, and any impediments to them identified.

Even more important to the conferees, perhaps, was the emergence of the strong and positive role to be played by fertilizer. This consciousness brought the conference very close to its purpose, close to the role that IMC had so early perceived for the industry in the face of the overwhelming pressure for additional food supplies. Fertilizer alone could do a lot, they knew, and without it very little else could be done. There were other agricultural wonders, to be sure, but in terms of the many problems being made visible at the conference, the role of these other marvels was somewhat longer range. It took time to develop a backup system for the successful introduction of modern farm machinery. It took time to carry farmer credit down the worn trails and footpaths to the farmers in greatest need of it. But it was not hard to convincingly demonstrate the value of fertilizer to the soil and—within one growing season—improve yield enormously:

".. . With all due respect to seeds and chemicals and tractors, at this moment in man's history fertilizer represents the best medium for immediate and sizable alleviation of the world hunger problem.

"Let me cite just one example that illustrates this conclusion. Last year FAO, which is an instrument of the United Nations, conducted 9,500 demonstration plots in 14 different countries. Nothing was changed from the preceding year; the seed was the same, the chemicals were the same, the farmers were the same, everything was the same—except the amount of fertilizer applied. It was increased to a more respectable level. At the end of the year more than 70 percent increase was shown in the amount of food realized on those demonstration plots as compared to the preceding year. In other words, we almost doubled the amount of food produced on the same amount of ground just by the change in fertilizers in a short period of 12 months. That's why we conclude that at this time fertilizer is the best medium for making the greatest gains in the shortest period of time. So it is obvious that the world fertilizer industry has an obligation to examine the ways and means by which it might bring its resources together and produce food more abundantly and more economically, because within these resources lies the best answer for producing the greatest amount of food . . ."

. . . from conference proceedings, 1968

And that expressed the moving spirit behind the conferences. It was a transformed corporate molecule, beginning to expand to include the consciousness of those who came in contact with it. Its force was undeniable. The direction of activity for those present changed but little; it was the goal of the industry that had changed in the process and that, of course, changed the meaning of everything else.

It provided a moment of great quiet pride for IMC, when a conferee first stood up and said:

"It is certainly a great pleasure to be part of an industry whose objectives are those of bettering the conditions of man . . ."

. . . from conference proceedings, 1966

But it was not pride, nor pleasure, which IMC sought through the conferences. The purpose remained unequivocally the same. Four years of conferences had made the ever so slight dent in the thinking of world leaders who had the same devotion to help, as did IMC. The more significant breakthrough was the simple fact that the problems were laid bare. They could no longer be ignored.

Negative? Perhaps. Disheartening? Indeed. Because the problem is so complex and of such magnitude that it overwhelmed those who suddenly awakened to its true and frightening significance and tried to attack it with a view to quick solution. There could be no quick solution. There was not even a single completely defined route to the amelioration of the problem.

What sustained IMC's decision to continue the conferences was the general agreement that whatever emerged as a plan must include the maximum production of food worldwide through the application of fertilizer. It was the undeniable answer.

Yet IMC made the decision with the full realization that neither it nor any other single organization could do more than its knowledge and resources permit and having already solicited and obtained the concern of world leaders, the template for the future was drawn.

On the broad middle ground where these obligations were defined clearly by IMC and the conference participants, there was room for action. All else was out in the open. Now it was time to do something . . . to move. Literally, there was no turning back now. The fertilizer industry was completely changed. The world was enlightened. The momentum had just begun. IMC turned its face to the future.

the conferences
...an amalgam of awareness

A particularly positive result of the early meetings was that industry concerns most relevant to the problem of hunger had clarified and the World Food Production Conferences took on a new level of meaning. Originally those assembled were mainly representative of the fertilizer industry; by the time of the third conference there were significant numbers of observers from other sectors of the economy.

In Latin America there were bankers, business people, educators, the press, radio and TV, as well as ambassadors and diplomats from various of its countries. These were in addition to the panelists themselves, who represented more than 80 percent of the productive power of the fertilizer industry of Latin America.

And the third Asia/Pacific meeting attracted its observers as well. They represented various departments of the Australian government, people from the U.S. Department of Agriculture, A.I.D., dignitaries from the Australian Freedom from Hunger Campaign, and the United Nation's Food and Agriculture Organization. The FAO representative's presence was quite a compliment to the conference as he had been directed by FAO headquarters in Rome to attend the session and make a full report of the deliberations. The report was to be officially presented to the annual National World Assembly of FAO people in Rome within a few weeks.

The attraction of such distinguished observers, and especially that the U.N. had exhibited this kind of interest, was a welcome indication that the urgency and activities of the conference were not falling on deaf ears.

It was fortunate they were not, for conditions had changed drastically during those first three years. There had been both an acceleration of crop yields and a great diminution of existing grain reserves. The American agricultural economy, in particular, had been turned upside down.

At the time the First World Food Production Conference was launched, American agriculture suffered from restrictive controls and deflationary, depressive actions. The U.S. was faced with food surpluses . . . and millions of acres of idle land. Good arable land, idle. Rich land that had been withdrawn from cultivation. There were low prices, which made it difficult for the farmer to survive. And there were barriers that precluded the free flow of food from surplus areas to deficient areas.

The result was the shameful coexistence of surpluses and hunger in the world at the same time.

By the time the third conference got under way, surpluses were history! They no longer existed! The United States was allocating free exports to various needy nations around the world, and the allocations were falling below the commitments originally made. The giant potential of American agriculture was recalled into service, though it was not a giant that knew no fear. With its own grain reserves all but gone, and many hungry parts of the world now looking to it for food, American agriculture got busier than it had been in years. Millions of acres of idle land were returned to cultivation. In 1966, it was 30 million acres, and the following year another 30 million. The price of grain increased.

And there were reports of other, if smaller scale, food production increases beginning to overcome traditional practices, that were brought to the conference:

"As you know, throughout Latin America agriculture has been regarded more as a traditional way of life than as a potentially profitable business, or a necessary foundation for the development of a modern economy . . . Only an estimated 10 percent of total annual investment flows into the agriculture sector in Latin America.

"A recent study by the Inter-American Development Bank estimates that a 5 percent annual growth in agricultural output could increase per capita income in the rural areas by about $60 per year . . . a substantial improvement over the current average of less than $200 per year in the rural areas of Latin America.

"In Mexico, agriculture has registered a substantial growth in the last calendar year, and Mexico is now a net exporter of agricultural products. Last year corn exports were up 36.5 percent; tomato exports up 28.5 percent, and coffee up 10 percent. Mexico has also moved from a wheat-deficient to a wheat-exporting nation. These improvements are due in no small measure to the important advances made in the use of fertilizer in Mexico."

. . . from conference proceedings, 1967

It was difficult to determine just which elements of forceful energy combined to produce progress, but it had not happened in a vacuum. While it could not be said that increases in food production happened only *because* of the conferences, there was a definite belief in some relationship between the two. If nothing more, the conferences had permanently altered the environment of food production, for they had initiated international discussions aimed at measuring what could be done about world hunger. They had taken the measure of the talents of the fertilizer industry, and the tools it had available. Initially, the major contributions of the World Food Production Conferences had been merely that they brought together a forceful group to challenge the pessimistic, defeatist approach that had dominated all previous discussions of the world hunger problem . . . particularly in the developed nations.

When the conferences had begun, there were important schools of thought that included some very vocal professors in some of the finer universities in the United States, who had already agreed that famine was inevitable. Now, within a few years, enough evidence had developed to indicate that if famine occurred in the future, it would be because of disgraceful neglect, and that it *would* be possible to avoid it if the appropriate resources assumed their rightful share of responsibility.

There was a general awareness at the conferences that the major segment of this responsibility bore on the world fertilizer industry. Certainly, if famine were to recur within the next decade, the most serious failure would be on the part of the fertilizer industry of the world, because it alone possessed the latitude for helping farmers make their greatest gains over the shortest period of time.

And yet, the conferees found, every time this simple improvement of fertilizer was discussed—with its known ability to increase food production in multiples—there was always someone who would ask, "Well, are you really in this to save man, or are you in this to make a profit?"

IMC, particularly, was pressed with this probing of its motives in the early conference years. It found that the question could be answered only by the elemental reminder that within the private enterprise system in which it operates, it- or any company—could be effective only if it remained prosperous. If it didn't, its resources would become ineffective, its ability to contribute to greatly increased food production would diminish and its overall impact would become minimal. And that, whether involved in government or private facilities, each member of the fertilizer industry had dual obligations to maximize the exploitation of its resources: in an economic sense—so it could grow and increase those resources; and in a humane sense—so those resources could be used to produce more food.

Business was not only business, it was also a factual part of the world. Businessmen were not only businessmen, but were also human beings, with human concerns.

This was the major underpinning of the IMC philosophy that first led to the conferences. The philosophy was taking hold and beginning to expand through the industry. That change, it was believed, was in part responsible for the hope of great progress in the near future. It was clearly expressed by one of the conferees:

> "I guess that most of us have been trying to bring the future into focus since we were old enough to recognize that planned objectives bring more formidable results, and that, if we amble along giving in to circumstantial pressures without resistance, we lose sight of our destination. So—I would like to feel that we are not only bringing the future into focus, but that we also plan to shape that future. In this room today is sufficient brain power, business savvy, influence in political circles, and representation of capital resources to not only envision the future of food production in Latin America, but individually and collectively to create enough conviction to determine the future of fertilizer production and distribution in Latin America.
>
> "There is no other area of business which satisfies more completely the joint desire of contributing to the improvement of mankind, and of making a healthy, selfish profit.
>
> "When we first received IMC's invitation to attend this conference, we experienced mixed emotions as to their objectives. Doubts lingered that IMC might want to know our plans in order to improve their own competitive position in Latin America. But, having attended other sessions of this type promoted by IMC, we have become convinced that they truly wish to act as a catalyst for general analysis and preparation for the fertilizer revolution now with us, and ahead of us. The future fertilizer demand factors, the custom of trading raw materials and end products within the industry, and the common problems of farmer education—these

together convinced us of IMC's motive to promote the general growth of the fertilizer industry. We appreciate being a part of this distinguished group."

. . . from conference proceedings, 1967

It was important to create a unifying rallying point among international producers of fertilizer, in order to change the environment of food production. And it was equally important to help change the manner in which governments dealt with one another in regard to food supplies. Very practical plans for improving education, credit, fertilizer and other modern farming methods needed to be implemented on a scale that was well beyond the reach of the private sector.

How this might be accomplished, and what the conference role in such undertakings might be, was brought out in a stunning example:

"*. . . In order to get the best results in overcoming the problem we are facing, the way is to get multilateral international cooperation among the developed countries.*

"*For one example, the Japanese Government is now trying to set up an Agricultural Development Fund for Southeast Asia. During the period of April to August this year, the Second Cabinet Members Conference for developing Southeast Asia is scheduled in Manila. Japan is to sponsor the establishment of (a fund of) about $300 million and try to complete the setup by September of this year.*

"*The fund will be used for 1) increasing food production, 2) improving of agricultural techniques, 3) bettering the agricultural land, and 4) uplifting the will and the way of life of working farmers for better productivity.*

"*At the same time, our government is establishing a corporation under Government risk and account to develop primary products in developing countries and to improve importation in Japan, with the Government taking the risks for non-delivery, and any claim against quality, and market risks factors which have been the main stumbling blocks preventing commercial firms from going into long-term purchase contracts.*

"*I think we can all urge our governments to take the initiative in participating in an international organization to help developing countries, taking all means and opportunity available, not least by raising public interest and opinion.*

"For this purpose, I believe this World Food Production Conference is executing a most efficient part of our need for prompt action, and I am glad I am able to participate in it."

. . . from conference proceedings, 1967

These external changes in the environment of food production were considered to be of value in the largest sense. They were exciting and motivating to the conferees. And yet, it was important that the primary focus of activity—and result—remain within the direct area of conference expertise.

Helping governments to understand they have a major role in taking the risks was one very important thing.

For industry to find ways to help minimize those risks was another. Cutting back the costs was something in which industry had a direct role, and the conference was vital in bringing the valuable experience of a fertilizer supplier in one country to suppliers in other countries around the world.

Here's the way it happened. This was considered typical of practical conference results:

CHAIRMAN: "Before we get into the subject that's scheduled for this morning, I think it would be worthwhile to have some comments regarding the whole subject of distribution—physical distribution—which was handled late yesterday afternoon without benefit of discussion.

"Not only must we be able to physically move ever-increasing volumes of fertilizer raw materials and products, but we must also move the end products. And we must be able to do it economically, expeditiously, and at the right time. There's only one growing season a year, and there isn't much we can do about that except to be prepared with all the necessary raw materials at the time the planting season occurs, because if it goes on by us we lose a whole year. Remember, always, that we're dealing in the fertilizer area with low-cost bulk materials, wherein the cost of transportation frequently exceeds—sometimes by several times—the cost of the product itself.

"*I'm certain in the United States the most neglected area in all industries—particularly in raw materials—has been the area of physical distribution. If we dedicate ourselves with the same intelligence and enthusiasm that we do in other areas, I'm sure that the costs of distribution can be whittled down as much as 30 percent to 50 percent below present levels. So we're not dealing with an area of little significance, either economically or otherwise. I don't know of another area where we could expend our energy and intellect to more productive use. To repeat some of the basic facts that were brought out:*

"*One of the factors that plagues us, and this involves both the developed and less-developed nations, is the total inadequacy of deep-water ports. This is particularly critical because one of the available avenues that can greatly reduce the cost of water transportation is the use of larger and larger vessels. But they can't be used unless they can get into port. This is a problem that faces the Florida phosphate field. It's a problem that faces many of the ports to which the product is shipped. Australia is a case in point. So are South America and other areas of the world. What are some of the thoughts in Japan today to improve the efficiency and the economy of distribution?*"

CONFEREE: "*As you know, Japan is a small country and we have many factories. Lately all the ammonium sulphate manufacturers made an agreement between themselves so as to save on their transportation charges. They decided something like this: orders coming from any area must be delivered from the nearest producer despite any nominated brand the buyer wants to buy. That means something like no (trade) mark at all on ammonium sulphate. This just started two years ago, and I think this method is saving quite a lot of distribution charges for both the producer and the consumer.*"

CHAIRMAN: "*Very significant factor. Even if a customer placed an order with Maker A, but if Maker B is closer, it is shipped from Maker B's supply?*"

CONFEREE: "*That's right.*"

CHAIRMAN: "*And then Maker A will sometimes ship for Maker B? That's a very important breakthrough.*"

. . . from conference proceedings, 1967

Results are very hard to measure, but it was the aim of the conference to achieve results. Practical results. The conceptual

result desired was to see the production of food leap forward
and be directed into the hands of the hungry. But that is impractical. It is a motivational desire, not an achievable one.
The sponsors were keenly aware that the conference pebble
being dropped into the ocean of need would not immediately
raise the level of food production. Nevertheless, they did hope
that the concentric rings resulting from the splash would move
outward to energize and motivate others. The task of education,
for example, underscored every practical objective. Almost
nothing could be achieved directly, unless there was an educational and communication component attached to it.

The ideas generated by the conference were exciting, but to
turn them into practical results, they all required the same catalyst: money. A developing understanding of just how—in one
form or another—money might best become fused into the
struggle led to some very practical undertakings aimed at increasing the production of food:

> *"We talked about educating the banker. Shouldn't one of us obli-
> gate himself to take a number of bankers in a given area and find
> out from each what are the things that affect his mind, and why
> agriculture has such a low level of attraction for his funds, and
> what we can do to stimulate and educate him? In other words, after
> a very stimulating, exciting meeting, my appeal here is that, be-
> cause we are all men of authority and stature and decision and
> action, we obligate ourselves in an experimental way to do one or
> two of these little things over the next twelve months. IMC will
> certainly serve in whatever capacity as a collector and disseminator.
> We will, wherever possible and wherever feasible, use our personnel
> to aid and abet your efforts so that next year we can take a look
> at the progress we've made in some of these areas."*

> *. . . from conference proceedings, 1968*

Money, the most practical of all objects, the catalyst for all
goods and services, thus took on new dimensions at the World
Food Production Conferences. The entire plan for increasing
food production was based on looking ahead. Not so far ahead
as to be impractical, but at least toward the next growing season. There were plans discussed that included moving seeds and

fertilizer—and enough education to use them—into the farmers' fields. It could done but not without money.

However, the absence of money could have a less harmful effect if money could be thought of and considered in conceptual terms. That is, if it could be supplied without being present. If it could be supplied as an idea; the idea would only become a reality at the end of the next growing season. The term for using this concept of money effectively is credit.

Credit—money in its idea form—comprised one of the more creative results of conference discussion:

> *"At last year's Food Production Conference, one subject eventually became a common denominator, appearing and reappearing like a refrain in the statements of the speakers.*
>
> *"This was the problem of credit. In one case, credit was referred to as the 'great void' in food production planning.*
>
> *"If credit is to meet the actual needs of the small and medium sized farmer, it must be appropriately linked to the growing cycles.*
>
> *"As the representative of one country declared flatly: 'With enough credit, we could double the use of fertilizer in one year.' The consensus was that credit was an increasingly vital ingredient in any effort to bring about higher production. And that there was need for better knowledge of all the credit systems as they might have been tried, or were presently in force, in all Latin America.*
>
> *"IMC agreed to conduct a survey in order to find out in an authoritative way just what credit practices are most successful in each Latin American country.*
>
> *"So last July the information gathering got underway. IMC worked through the Rural Development Officers attached to the U.S. Embassies in 20 different countries—Mexico, the Caribbean, Central and South America.*
>
> *"The response gave a strong indication of how important credit is. Some of the programs described are extremely sophisticated and very inclusive. Others are so simple as to be only mildly effective.*
>
> *"But each is recognizable as a program with some sort of structure, an announced goal, and certain mechanisms for putting everything in motion.*
>
> *"We think some of you may find it of interest to review the entire report. And copies of it will be distributed to you today, as well as a small folder entitled 'Blueprint for Farm Credit'.*
>
> *". . . with adequate credit available to him, along with technical*

instruction, a farmer can increase his use of fertilizers dramatically. This, as the United Nations has pointed out, constitutes the most direct and practical way for any country to combat hunger and improve living standards . . ."

. . . from conference proceedings, 1968

Perhaps the greatest clarity achieved by the conference was in the area of developing true perceptions of the state of the art of agriculture as it really was. Here, agriculture was not denuded into statistics, but always had upon it a sense of the sweat of toil, of the struggle of the farmer—who was, worldwide, considered a relatively simple and uncomplicated human with a profound and natural love of the soil. With that temperament he was somewhat at the mercy of the more modern world around him. His location was rural, while the modern world was growing in the urban centers. Worldwide, the farmer's education was minimal, while the modern world's most significant progress has been made by those trained in the universities. The farmer was a model of earthy simplicity, while the modern world had grown to a sophistication that took astronauts to another celestial body, breaking free of the earth altogether.

In a broad sense then, the farmer—upon whom the basis of civilization rests—was badly in need of remedial attention. It was one focus of the conference to provide that remedial substance to the life of the farmer, to enable him to do the simple work upon which every sophistication of the world rested.

Neglected by the world for centuries, the conference brought news of that remedial progress, previously unknown:

"Little by little, the Chilean farmer has been using more and more fertilizers. To accomplish this we have used different methods. One of the best is the practical demonstration of fertilizer results in private and experimental plots—not those of the extension services and other private agencies, but those of progressive farmers. We conduct these demonstrations through cooperatives and regional farmer associations. Government agencies that promote these modern techniques have not had the desired results in Chile.

". . . In Chile we are trying to stress the farmer cooperative movement, both on a regional level and in specialized crops. Credit

facilities, especially those of the state bank, are enlisted in aid of this cooperative movement . . .

"Another way to increase the consumption of fertilizers by farmers has been the campaign to reduce fertilizer cost. The government has conducted this campaign with the purpose of searching for ways to reduce both the external and internal cost factors. I must thank International Minerals and Chemical Corporation for the mass of information and the surveys that we in Chile have received. It has helped us rationalize the internal distribution of fertilizers, and to reduce the cost of distribution of fertilizers. It has helped both the government agency and private enterprise to reach the farmer with lower prices, to which he is most responsive.

. . . from conference proceedings, 1967

Something was in the wind. Things were happening. Progress was undeniable. No one would be foolhardy enough to claim the progress was the direct result of the World Food Production Conference. There were far too many factors to even try to make a case for that. But there was no denying that a new sense of understanding existed, that a new mechanism for the transmission of information had been formed.

The corporate molecule that had transformed the goals of IMC's agricultural activities had generated sparks at the conference and was spreading. If the improvement in agricultural production could not be laid at the door of the conference, surely the enthusiasm with which it was reported could. For now there was a place to stand and say:

"The influences of agricultural production changes . . . have been analyzed as follows:

Excellent increases in agricultural production have been noted over the past three years;

New capital is flowing into the agricultural sector of the Brazilian economy; and

For the first time in the history of Brazil, agriculture is being supported by action programs from the government."

. . . from conference proceedings, 1967

There was a genuine excitement. It pervaded the conference, and was felt by the observers as well as the conferees. Word was getting out to the world that agriculture was not standing still. More importantly, food was getting to the hungry. Food that a few years previously did not exist. There was simply, and indisputably, more of it. And this was only the beginning. Everyone at the conference felt that. Whatever residue of early hesitation there was, was melting. It was clear that von Liebig now had a more powerful constituency than did Malthus. And it was not lying down and whining; it was standing firm and winning!

By the time of the Fourth World Food Production Conference, the picture was clear. The dismal trend was reversing itself. The availability of food was gaining on population.

The idea of success was taking hold. New ideas were jumping across national and continental boundaries, skipping across oceans more readily than they had once crossed.

"... One of the conclusions I came to at the first meeting (of the World Food Production Conference), when we were told about the use of the electronic computer for farming purposes, was the importance of preparing the country to be able to utilize this fantastic technological instrument. But to be able to use the computer we have to have all the basic information on soils, marketing, prices, ecological conditions and other factors. The State Bank, as a result of a seminar held by IMC, drew up a complete cadastral survey of its clients. These clients were recorded on a cadastral basis to check the level of cultivation, ecological and soil conditions, etc. This is the basic documentation that we need, in order to introduce computerization in agriculture. In other words, to be able to establish optimum programming for each of the states and regions. I came to this conclusion at a previous conference ... and we are now implementing this system in Chile with a view towards introducing computerization in the next few years."

... from conference proceedings, 1969

The conference was not a solid unit. It was made up of individuals. They came together in mutual respect to exchange ideas and information. To learn. To learn, and to teach. Each nation represented had special concerns, special situations and conditions that made its problems unique. But the ideas that were solving problems within those unique situations were, most often, applicable to others as well.

It was this honest dealing with ideas, this urgent sense of suggestion that made the conference a roomful of sparks, sizzling with energies that leapt from one person, one nation to another.

It was obvious and it was exciting. The conference chairman expressed it with modest eloquence:

> *"Innovation . . . and more innovation. There's always room for it. And in our business there's a continuing, desperate need for it, if we are to solve our problems and hold our course of progress.*
>
> *"Moreover, the industry as a whole can't come up with all the answers. Each individual on his own must catch onto this innovative spirit and put it to work in his special situation . . ."*
>
> *. . . from conference proceedings, 1968*

Innovation was not, of course, the property of the conference alone. Nor was concern for feeding the hungry, and developing nutrition beyond previously known limits.

And, in a unique presentation, this was brought before the conference. A report was made that contained a survey of startling new achievements of science and agriculture. These promised not only new availability of food, but also new food products, originating not only on the farm, but in the laboratory. Food that was the product, not only of agriculture, but of industry.

This presentation by an IMC spokesman not only re-painted the picture of need, but offered a new and fascinating summary of potential supplemental sources of nutrition.

It would have surprised von Liebig. It would have shamed Malthus. It fascinated the conferees:

> *"In this year's conference, as in those of the past, we all recognize that a vital element in food production is taking the farmer's harvest to market.*
>
> *"We also know that the farmer's crop can dramatically change*

its appearance and other characteristics from the time it is first harvested until the time it reaches the ultimate consumer.

"So, as we consider the alleviation of hunger throughout the world, we must realize that it's not only a matter of how much food, but what kind *of food is consumed . . . its nutritional value. Consider these facts:*

"Each day 10,000 people die from malnutrition. Most are children. Another two billion persons are physically or mentally retarded because of the same lack of nutrition. Of these 70 percent are children under six. Many don't even know they're hungry. They starve with full stomachs. Sound like a paradox? Let me explain.

"In parts of South America, the main diet consists of a manioc root flour that's cooked into a gruel. Those who eat only this feel well fed. But unlike diets of rice found in the East, and tapioca in India, manioc root gruel has no protein value whatever. The quantity *of food is sufficient; it's the* quality *that's so lacking.*

"Individuals who depend too much on these starchy gruels and grains cannot develop physically and mentally as they should. They're prone to debilitating nutritional diseases, and they lack the necessary vigor to confront their own problems, or even to care.

"This weakness particularly shows up in the sick and the injured, pregnant and lactating women, adolescents, and post-weaning children who develop an illness called "kwashiorkor" . . . an African word meaning "first-and-second," referring to the first child having been replaced at the breast by the second child. If the elder child's new diet has no cow's milk or protein equivalent, then impaired mental function is almost certain, and an early death is likely. Surely it is one of nature's greatest ironies that poverty begets poverty— a poverty of nutrition breeds a poverty of mind. Imagine destroying the intellect of millions of young people simply because they haven't received a few cents worth of protein in their daily diets!

"In India alone an estimated 35 percent to 40 percent of the 20 million babies born each year will have some degree of brain damage. One-third of that nation's population lacks sufficient protein. And even an end to their total food shortage will not fill their critical need. India's nutrition problems are further complicated by religious taboos. Although the country has one-fifth the world's cattle population, religious beliefs keep per capita consumption of beef the lowest of any major nation.

"Today this protein gap is second only to the total food supply problem. The United Nation's Food and Agriculture Organization (FAO) estimates that in a country where the food supply is marginal

the average individual needs 69 grams of total protein per day and 15 grams of animal or "good" protein. Based on this, by 1970—just two years away—the total protein deficiency in these hungry nations will be 10 million tons!

"To fill this gap we must tap the world's relatively large unused supply of protein. The knowhow and the raw materials are available and some work has begun. New foods are being constructed that are as nutritious as conventional protein sources, but more available, less costly, and acceptable to tastes and dietary habits. Let me tell you of some of the newest developments.

"Great progress has been made in building new foods using inexpensive high protein vegetable sources. One of the first of these is Incaparina which is marketed in Latin America, mainly in Guatemala and Colombia. The food is basically a cottonseed flour and corn mixture, with additives of locally available products such as tortula yeast and lysine.

"Retail price of the product is between 12 and 20 cents a pound, or about one-third of a U.S. cent per glass. It contains 27 percent protein which matches the nutritional value of powdered milk. Over five million pounds of Incaparina are consumed annually in the two countries, roughly the equivalent of 80 million glasses of milk or 100 million eggs.

"The Incaparina flour can be used to make colada, the traditional thin gruel of Colombia, as well as other dishes in which cornmeal is an ingredient. It was formulated to supplement diets with additional protein but it can serve as a sole protein source if necessary. The main difficulty is in persuading people to make the unfamiliar substance part of their diets.

"Similar formulas are being introduced in many other parts of the world.

"Soybeans, which are very high in protein, are being converted into a highly palatable flour by a new process. Containing 40 percent protein and 20 percent fat, the flour can be used in beverages, soups, and many cooked dishes. Other oilseeds, including sesame, sunflower and safflower seeds, and coconut and palm nuts are also valuable as protein sources.

"Beverages containing soy flour are a nutritious food for babies and small children past the weaning stage. Sugar, flavoring, or juices from local fruits can be added for taste and additional nutrients.

"Soybean milk substitutes are becoming available in the United States in a move to offset the high cost of dairy products. The cow is a notoriously inefficient and expensive producer of milk, and

manufacturers are discovering an equally palatable and far cheaper milk can be manufactured from all-vegetable ingredients. The product can be powdered, but is sold mainly as a liquid dairy product. In nutrition the vegetable milk equals cow's milk.

"In Peru, an experimental soft drink called Peruvita was not a profitable venture. Its failure was attributed to cheap formulation which slighted acceptability and taste.

"Another product used in beverages, or cooked into gruel, is a high protein corn-soya-milk food supplement called CSM. Mixed with a sweetened, flavored gelatine it is a great success with children. It can also be prepared as a custard dessert, used as an additive to soup, or mixed with water to form a smooth dough which can be made into unleavened bread like Mexican tortillas or Asian chapati.

"The product is a mixture of 70 percent processed precooked cornmeal, 25 percent toasted defatted soy flour, and five percent nonfat dry milk with vitamins and minerals added. One pound represents about 1,650 calories and contains 20 percent protein.

"Last month the Coca-Cola Company announced it had developed a protein-based chocolate flavored drink which it will produce and test market in Brazil. In January, the Yoo Hoo Beverage Corporation announced it had made a breakthrough in the development of a formula for a high-protein drink which it will produce and sell in foreign countries.

"Currently the Pillsbury Company is working on a high-protein beverage in El Salvador. In Brazil, Krause Milling Company is experimenting with fortified corn products, Swift and Company is looking for high protein foods, and Monsanto Chemical is developing a high-protein beverage made of soybeans.

"Even more intriguing are the new solid proteins spun or extruded to resemble meats and other foods. They generally can take several shapes including chips, chunks, flakes, granules, or puffs.

"One major U.S. supplier of soybean products just opened a new processing plant for its TVP or textured vegetable protein. This substance contains 50 percent protein, 32 percent carbohydrates, and less than one percent fat. It can be made to look like beef, chicken, ham or bacon, and can be given nut, fruit, and spice flavors for other food applications.

"Hydrated TVP can be chopped into patties, ground into meatballs, or used as a food ingredient like cubed chicken. This remarkable product not only supplies the food value of meat but also tastes like meat—something many hungry people rarely get to enjoy.

"Similar to TVP is the isolated soy protein or ISP, now being

made by several other U.S. companies with up to 100 percent protein content, in forms resembling meats and seafoods. There is also a bright future for ISP products as completely new foods, with their own identities, rather than as imitations of meats and poultry products.

"At General Mills, in the United States, isolated soy protein research has led to the spinning of high purity oilseed protein into monofilaments, to provide a textural basis for foods.

"The process begins by upgrading 55 percent soybean meal to 97 percent pure protein. This protein is then dispersed in alkali, and precipitated at the isoelectric point in a bath by drawing it away continuously from the face of spinnerets, much the same way as for rayon or nylon.

"As a result of the spinning process, a monofilament of pure protein is created. At this stage the fibrils have not been given any chemical hardening or any other treatment.

"The fibrils can be sized and further processed to create any texture desired. For instance, they can create the texture of steak, ham, bacon, chicken, or any other food popular to a given locale.

"Now the fibrils are combined with such standard edible items as wheat gluten, egg albumin, vegetable or animal fats, flavors, and dyes, for fortification, flavor, and color.

"The end products are not considered substitutes, but rather 'food analogs'. In manufacture, bulk amounts—such as bacon analogs—can be produced for about half the cost of the actual food product. And they possess far more protein per unit. After cooking, the products can be immediately used, or stored by refrigeration, freezing, canning, or drying.

"Certainly one of the most impressive aspects of these food analogs is their versatility. They can be tailored to be palatable to every taste. What's more, they can be made to meet the most rigid dietary requirements—zero cholesterol, vegetarian, Kosher—in fact, any diet imposed for medical, cultural, or religious reasons.

"Still another pure protein product is the single cell protein or SCP. It is a simple type of organism with a high amino acid content, and comes from a yeast grown in crude petroleum. SCP is now being produced in Scotland and France to grow a nearly tasteless, odorless, white protein powder which can be made into sophisticated imitations of standard human food, ranging from meat concentrates and cookies, to Vietnamese fish sauce.

"Creating these totally new foods, either from pure protein substances or from vegetable bases, is just one way of enriching man's

diet. Another way the protein gap is being filled is by fortification of existing grains with protein concentrates, synthetic amino acids which build other proteins, and vitamins. For example, a few dollars of lysine added to one ton of wheat raises its protein quality to more nearly that of casein or milk protein.

"This fortification is a less conventional approach than the growing of those grains that have high lysine content, but it has great short-run advantages, and since it requires no change in dietary and consumption patterns, it's well-suited to reduce protein deficiencies in the non-meat eating parts of the world.

"Another way to improve protein sources in many parts of the developing world would be to make oilseeds, such as soybean, cottonseed and peanuts, indigenous crops to those areas, for oilseeds have the potential of furnishing almost as much protein for man as that available from animal sources. Attempts are underway now, for instance, to see to what extent soybeans can be grown in India, Pakistan, South America and Africa.

"No report on the developments in adding protein to hungry diets would be complete without some mention of the strides being taken in the field of animal agriculture. Production of greater quantities of animal products is a natural way to help improve the world's protein nutrition. Man has traditionally improved the balance of his diet of plant materials by adding meat, milk, and eggs.

"World food planners often discount the contributions livestock and poultry make to the food supply. Presumably they believe increases in animal production necessitate the use of human food that might better go into the human diet. Today, however, we're discovering that livestock can exist largely on feeds unsuitable for human consumption—forage, by-products and waste.

"Currently many feedstuffs are not being fully utilized in hungry countries. Residues from food grains such as corn, wheat, rice, sorghums, oats, and barley are useful feeds which are often ignored. Vegetable wastes, sugar beet byproducts, cottonseed meals, gin waste, extracted sugarcane, spent brewery grains, and molasses are examples of products adaptable to animal feeds. Animal by-products, like meat scraps, fats, tankage, and bonemeals, and even certain manures, can become nutrition for livestock.

"The genetic approach to improving livestock and poultry production in hungry nations is also being used. This doesn't mean direct exportation of U.S. or European breeds to other parts of the world. Instead, it involves the slower process of upgrading native breeds through crossbreeding with imported stock.

"Improving animal feeding efficiency—that is raising the ratio of pounds of feed to pounds of meat produced—is another way to increase protein availability. If the efficiency of world animal production could be improved only four percent, more than five million acres of land would be released for production of other crops for human food.

"Fish harvesting, too, can provide immense amounts of protein. About one billion tons of fish populate the seas, but of this total 950 million tons go free. We catch and consume only about 50 million tons a year.

"New commercial fishing technology, plus the enormous commercial potential in fish protein concentrate, are beginning to change these figures.

"Most of these developments I have covered are short-range approaches to filling the protein gap. Many already are being implemented in the world's hungry nations. Those still in the experimental stage are likely to be in practice in the near future.

"But progress thus far and in the future, is not without problems. There will continue to be difficulties in getting the malnourished and hungry to accept nutritious foods, for people the world over are reluctant to change consumption patterns just because something is good for them. New food products must be sold on other merits in addition to their protein content.

"But the world must turn to the new foods if we are to tip the balance between the population explosion and food shortages, and to strengthen the quality of the diets of the undernourished. The vicious cycle of poverty and hunger can be broken if we provide ample protein for the world's undernourished children. New diets can deliver them from mental and physical retardations that malnutrition now fosters.

"New high-protein foods may not be the panacea we're all searching for. But we can hope that they will make a major contribution in changing man's food resources to better meet the demands of an ever-growing hungry world."

. . . from conference proceedings, 1968

the conferences
...a symposium of success

It would be misleading to imply that the world's food supply increased swiftly and surely from the time of the founding of the World Food Production Conference. It did not. Agriculture and its corollaries reflect only the response of man to nature. But nature and man are still far from the mutual understanding that would assure a steadily abundant, and virtually unlimited, food supply. It is nature who conducts the concert; the farmer can play his land only as well as he is able under those circumstances. And every year the world-audience must wait to learn if the performance will include a seat for everyone—at the table.

Winds and rains are subject to the vagaries of time, and timing is everything to the farmer. Too much, too soon, too little, and too late; these are the phrases that create the farmer's stoicism. He tries. The farmer always tries. But sometimes he cannot even coax so much as a minimal yield from his land.

To be sure, the charts showed food production was clearly rising, but that meant in aggregate, in total . . . not in every case. Sometimes nature's quirks were worrisome, but harmless. Other times, they put the lives of millions in jeopardy. A report of such a tragedy reached the Third Asia Pacific Conference:

> "When I last had the privilege of addressing you briefly in Tokyo in February of 1966, I concluded my short address with the following words:
>
>> 'We, therefore, have in India today not only the task before us of feeding the population of the largest democracy in the world, but also the prospects of having the means to do so well within our grasp.'
>
> "Since these words were spoken, disaster has struck India in the form of exceptional and unfavorable weather conditions, and the progress which I optimistically forecast has not been possible. As a

result, the country continues to suffer a grave deficit of foodstuffs for the current year. The weather conditions which I refer to as having affected the 1966 crops are not to be regarded as something very exceptional. The lesson of this experience is twofold: not only must the harvest grow more each year than the consumption of its rapidly growing population; but the country must also have an available buffer of not less than 25 million tons of food grains to meet the shortfall of lean years such as 1966. The setback which we have experienced need, nevertheless, be only temporary, and I do not propose to modify my words of last year even in the smallest degree. One reason for my confidence is the growing appreciation on all sides of the importance of the use of fertilizer to achieve crop levels in keeping with the country's requirements . . .

. . . from conference proceedings, 1967

The conference was not only aware of the struggle—it considered itself part of the struggle.

Its involvements were practical, as far as helping transform the ways of men in the production of food. But it was helpless against nature in specific places. Even so, the bad news came padded with a new kind of understanding which recognized that specific crop failures were setbacks, not reversals.

There were places in the world where people still died from hunger and malnutrition in large numbers, but the numbers—though large—were becoming smaller. And though people by the millions were still feeling the sharp teeth of hunger gnawing at them from the inside, there were fewer of them, and fewer teeth in the hunger. For the most part the worst problems were now confined to areas that had suffered local disaster. Reserves had not yet built up enough; neither had the social mechanisms to deal with such problems. Still, there was a reversal of a trend occurring, if not yet a complete resolution of the problem.

After several years of struggle, a new trumpet of hope was being heard at the conference. It was sounded loudly and clearly by a co-chairman in his keynote address:

"Gentlemen, as we commence our fifth World Food Production Conference, we have every reason to rejoice in our efforts of the

past and in our prospects for the future. Indeed, the entire world can find occasion to join us in that rejoicing. For if we have not dispelled the doubts of a few, we have most certainly convinced the minds of many that the world's food crisis can be averted. The facts are now arousing the attention of those people whose help we desperately need in order to continue our efforts with increasing success.

"In newspapers and magazines, the results of our efforts, and the efforts of others in this fight against hunger, are creating headlines and enthusiastic reports from the field. Scarcely a day passes that we don't see a news story praising our accomplishments. In the darkness of tragic events, which too often crowd the front pages, stories of increased world food production are most certainly a ray of light—a glimmer of hope for a new day with food enough for all.

"According to FAO, world food production rose three percent in 1967. More significantly, food production in developing nations increased by nearly six percent. These increases ranged from five percent in Latin America, to four percent in the Near East, to six percent in Africa and the Asia/Pacific area. Food production was up three percent in the United States and six percent in Western Europe. In the Soviet Union and Eastern communist block countries, food production declined slightly . . ."

. . . Keynote address, 1969

The mood was cautious, but not qualified. The pride was apparent, but not immodest, for it came from the background of effort. Those present knew of the conference focus, of the conference dedication, and of the conference pride in having engendered a determination for results. They also knew that a substantial part of the result lay in garnering aid from everywhere and helping it focus on the production of food. To the participants, it was a heartening sound—a trumpet of hope. And understandably so, for it was playing their song:

"In appraising our efforts thus far, I would say that the race to avert world famine is being won. And this is good news, because it means that we've come from behind and that we're ahead—in spite of those who said we didn't have a chance. And because we have

come from behind to first catch up and then pull ahead of the population explosion, I think it is safe to say that world food production will continue to increase its lead.

"As far as the future is concerned, it is appropriate to acknowledge recent developments in other areas of food production and then consider the things we should do and accomplish in the immediate years ahead.

"Scientists of every discipline are coming to our aid. We are aware of the tremendous strides occurring in developing new hybrids and new varieties. Thanks to the efforts of the International Rice Research Institute, for example, the Philippines is today self-sufficient in that staple for the first time since 1903.

"The excellent new wheat varieties, which have made Mexico self-sufficient in wheat—as well as new corn hybrids—are now creating self-sufficiency and even surpluses for export in India, in Pakistan, and in other nations in that area. Unlike some of the new high-yielding cereals in the United States and Japan, which were developed for rather specific growing conditions, these new varieties are adapted to a much broader range of latitudes.

"They are almost all short-stemmed, so they can absorb large quantities of fertilizer without danger of eventual lodging. They are much more responsive to fertilizer at all levels of application. A given amount of fertilizer produces a much greater increase in yield than with the older varieties of grain.

"New varieties of rice are early maturing, ripening in about 120 days compared with up to 180 days required by the older varieties. Also, they're rather insensitive to the length of daylight. So they can be planted at any time of year, providing prevailing temperatures and water supply permit. With adequate water, some farmers in the Philippines and India are harvesting two, or even three crops a year. Where water supplies are not sufficient to grow rice during the dry season, the farmers grow high-yielding grain sorghums or hybrid corn. Under actual field conditions this is resulting in yields as high as eight tons of grain per acre per calendar year. By comparison, two tons per acre is normally considered an excellent yield."

. . . Keynote address, 1969

The report that improved agriculture had led to increased food production was made up of many factors, obviously, but among them one thing stood out. And that one thing was dearest to the hearts of those present. It was a reasonable return on their faith in fertilizer as a catalyst for food production. As they had forecast, fertilizer was a basic and necessary ingredient of progress. It was exciting to see this promise on its way to fulfillment, exciting to see the world's food basket increase in size. But more food was not the only object of their quest, for food itself was only one factor in the war against hunger. There was also malnutrition, something that often fastened itself even within those who were no longer starving. Fortunately, progress was noted against malnutrition as well. Science was a notable ally of agriculture, and its aid had long since been enlisted to fight side by side in the battle. A new report from that front produced excitement as well:

> *"At last year's Food Production Conference, I was very pleased to report to you that food nutrition was receiving greater attention—especially in the case of protein. This is critically important because there are some areas of the world where children never develop to their physical and mental capacity because of the lack of protein and other essentials in their diets.*
>
> *"Protein involves a number of different amino acids. If even one of these is missing, human beings do not receive the nutritive value of protein. IMC scientists have made important contributions in the development of high-lysine corn—lysine being one of the most essential amino acids. In Western Canada, wheat and wild rye have been combined to create a cereal grain known as Triticale, a food high in protein.*
>
> *"For years and years, people claimed that no single corn hybrid could be developed which contained all the needed amino acids. But today, such a corn hybrid exists. And this may eventually prove to be one of the greatest breakthroughs of all."*
>
> *. . . Keynote address, 1969*

The keynote address at the Fifth World Food Production Conference was, in fact, a summary of successful activity. Each component of agriculture had been improved. More food and more nutrition were already working their way into the commerce of the world . . . and into the bodies of its inhabitants.

Still, the original problem of world population growth persisted in the minds of many as a potential force that could overshadow, and ultimately overcome, the progress that was being made. It was still, they believed, a clear and present danger. Von Liebig's spirit was now roaming free (and far and wide) with nearly rampant enthusiasm. But its nemesis, the spirit of Malthus, still hovered on the fringe of consciousness. Without blaming poor, long-dead Malthus, nor unfairly hanging on his memory the spectre of the necessity of starvation, the world needed to know just where population stood in relation to the progress reported in food gains.

The weight of Malthusian doom had first to be arrested and relieved of its terror before the world could be certain that each meal would not be the last for growing numbers of human beings.

Expanding population, the major pressure point implied by the conference's founding, needed to be accounted for. And it was:

> "... In addition to the tangible increases of food production, there is also an increasing effort to control the population expansion. We can't ignore [indications deduced by experts] that the world's population will probably double by the year 2000. The prospect of feeding some seven billion people is really awesome, if not completely hopeless. Today there are signs, however, that we may be able to decrease the population growth to some extent.
>
> "For one thing, the problems caused by too large a population are receiving great attention from governments—especially from the leaders of rapidly developing nations. The Indian government has given family planning a top priority. It currently has a million new mouths to feed each and every month. In 1963, India spent only $1.8 million on family planning. This year (1969) it will spend about $41 million. It currently has 5,400 rural family planning centers and 8,500 sub-centers.
>
> "The Agency for International Development has also strongly encouraged family planning. As a matter of fact, AID support on family planning is increasing. In 1965, it allocated some $2.5 million for population control. In this fiscal year, it plans to spend $35 million, fourteen times as much ... "

> ... from conference proceedings, 1969

And so, with favorable winds blowing from the world of food production, and all signs hopeful, the conference had proved its major point. It was possible for man, with his existing knowledge and technology, to create sufficient food for the peoples of the earth. It was not necessary for people to starve simply because they were born into the world at an inopportune time.

But, it was recognized, this was only a first step. A necessary first step, certainly, that proved in actuality what previously had been only a calculation based on theory. Practical and pragmatic testing of the theory had proved it in the real world. The end of food production was not, as yet, in sight. There *could* be more and more.

But production was only part. The growth of food did not, by itself, mean that it would get into the mouths of those whose need for it was greatest.

The strongly positive reports on the current status of worldwide food production offered only a glimpse of a happier future for man. They only pointed the way to new challenges.

The conference then undertook consideration of a new responsibility, best stated by the theme that was adopted:

"Agricultural output must be accelerated greatly to meet the food requirements by the year 2000. But if the system cannot supply the needy consumer when he needs it, in a form in which he can use it, and at a price which he can afford, then higher food production will have little effect on the War on Hunger. We will have failed to recognize and effectively challenge these real-life problems that limit food for the world's hungry.

"As the Latin American Conference convenes for the fifth time, we ask the dedicated participants who are present to look to even broader vistas and consider those contributing elements beyond the mere production of food. Our tasks are not completed until the food we produce is effectively utilized or consumed by the needy."

. . . theme of the Fifth Latin American Food Production Conference, 1969

By the fifth year of the conferences, it was clear that the world it served was changing. Of that there was no doubt. Even the unhappy instance of India's sudden and severe famine reported earlier had now come, if not full circle, well around.

The same conferee who, two years earlier, had delivered the report of Indian crop failure in the face of nature's damage, now brought new word of that troubled spot:

> "Gentlemen, I am happy to be associated with the Asia-Pacific Food Production Conference again, and be able to participate in your deliberations with the knowledge that conditions are much more favorable in India today than they were when I last met you. There is, most definitely, a silver lining in what were once very dark clouds.
>
> "Two years ago, in Sydney, I referred to the setback which India had experienced the previous year, as a result of adverse weather conditions and the failure of the monsoon rains. That setback continued into 1967, so that the earlier anticipated improvement was seriously delayed, the deficit of foodstuffs continued, and reliance had to be placed on imports of very essential foodgrain. But I said that the setback would be only temporary, and I said so because of my confidence in the resilience of the people of India.
>
> "That optimism has been fully warranted . . ."
>
> . . . from conference proceedings, 1969

Similarly, from others of the Pacific states, the sound of reversal was heard. The progress reported by the keynote speaker was swiftly being confirmed by one after another of the conferees:

> "When we talk of food production in the Philippines, our breakthrough in rice production comes first to mind. Since the early 1900s, the Philippines has been a rice-importing country. While the aggregate population has been estimated to be growing at the rate of 3.2 percent a year, production, on the other hand, has lagged behind with an annual rate increase of only 1.7 percent. This disparity has resulted in an ever-widening gap between domestic production and consumption.
>
> "1968 was not only a year of self-sufficiency in our rice produc-

tion, but it is also the year when the Philippines acquired a new status—that of an international rice exporter!"

. . . from conference proceedings, 1969

"There are signs of progress in the application of science and improved technology on food production in the developing countries. There is also a sense of growing optimism that an accelerated increase in food production in the near future will soon balance production and consumption satisfactorily. Many food deficit countries in general, and of Asia in particular, have. been reporting good crops for two successive years; they now face a hard job to maintain levels achieved so far, and to cope with the changes, new pressures, and demands brought about by progress. Indonesia is just an example.

"The bumper rice harvest of 1968 has brought hope to Indonesia. Production did not meet demand in full and there was still a substantial import of food. However, the food situation was much more favorable than that of 1967.

"Rice production showed an increase of 14 percent and 16 percent above the respective 1967 and 1966 production figures . . ."

. . . from conference proceedings, 1969

"Japan's rice production in both 1967 and 1968 achieved a record 14,450,000 tons. This is about three times that of the 1880s when Japan first joined the international community as a modern nation.

"Yield per acre was 450 kilograms for 1968, an increase of more than 10 percent over the last ten years. Moreover, working hours for rice production declined in the same period. For every ten acres in 1959, 173 hours were required, this decreased to 132 hours, a reduction to two-thirds of the original time.

"In this manner, efficiency in Japanese rice production made conspicuous gains, and now maintains a high standard among rice producing countries. . . ."

. . . from conference proceedings, 1969

The sense of urgency aroused by the success so fully proclaimed at the conferences, led the Latin American contingent to seek a means of increasing it.

The success of the conference seemed, to those conferees, to be largely a result of the transmission of information between the parties—the conferees, the scientists, and the farmers.

The apparent gains needed to be consolidated and carried further. It appeared that the basic tool was in hand, and needed only to be used. That conference resulted in a resolution:

> "In recognition of the fact that agricultural development is dependent both upon coordinated growth of all segments of an economy and the need for prompt communication of such achievements, the Fifth Latin American Food Production Conference hereby resolves to launch a continuing program to stimulate new projects in pure and applied research, technology, distribution, finance, and other areas.
>
> "The conference also resolves to make all information about these programs available to the broadest possible audience, through all channels of communication."

> . . . from conference proceedings, 1969

By the time five years of conferences had passed the initial problem seemed to have diminished to a point where it no longer required the undivided attention of the participants.

Changes in the world agricultural situation were so noted, and so remarkable, it became time to look beyond the mere production of food. And not just in spirit, but with the sense of dedication that had earlier proved so successful.

This progression was brought into sharp focus by an IMC representative in his report:

> "As our chairman stated in his keynote address, we are succeeding in our war against hunger. Through meeting together, sharing ideas, and coordinating our actions, we have been able to create improvements in the distribution of fertilizer and we've seen fertilizer usage increase food production.
>
> "All of our efforts thus far can be termed "Phase I" because,

*collectively, they comprise the initial steps necessary to avert world
famine in the future. And while we must continue to take action in
this first phase, we must also define the second phase, and then
plan and act accordingly. I am proud to say that as we enter our
fifth year of cooperation we—as a group—are uniquely qualified
to enter Phase II.*

*"We are unique because few other groups have devoted them-
selves for so long to eradicating hunger in this world. And of those
few groups, I can't think of any who possess the power to act as
we do. Long ago, we agreed that with our vested authority we bore
the responsibility to take action.*

*"What is Phase II? In a single descriptive word, it is 'Market-
ing!' Now, let me define the term further. Obviously, our ability
to produce fertilizers has little meaning if we can't get them into
the hands of farmers or—for that matter—get them on their fields.
Similarly, the farmer's ability to produce food in increasing amounts
is of little meaning, unless that food can be put into the hands of
the people who need it . . ."*

. . . from conference proceedings, 1969

Introducing the word "marketing" into the conference so
strongly at this point—and in a manner calculated to alter the
focus of the following meetings—requires explanation, for it is
a word subject to much abuse and criticism. Its meaning here,
however, was made very clear by a conference co-chairman:

*"During past conferences you have been witness to IMC's philoso-
phy of marketing. I think that as simple a definition as could be
put to the word is this: marketing is that function which assumes
the responsibility for taking the product from the point at which
it is produced and delivering it to the point at which it is used. This
functional definition intends to imply a continuum from production to consumption. That is, a continuing, overall responsibility
for each and every segment in sequence. That is marketing . . ."*

. . . from conference proceedings, 1969

Inasmuch as the conferences had always been of a pragmatic

bent, covering agendas filled with practical matters, this did not disturb the basic conference concern. In point of fact, it added an underpinning of a new reality that would, as food production increased, be a more important factor. For food that does not reach the consumer who needs it is not—in a pragmatic sense—food at all.

Discussion of that principle helped to define the sense of the marketing needs that had been introduced into the conference:

> "Under certain circumstances, marketing would include both merchandising and advertising. Certainly such circumstances would be minimal in the case of the war on hunger.
>
> "And . . . this may be the reason that marketing itself has not been given a priority position on the list of things which must be done. Why should it be important to merchandise or advertise the availability of food to those who are in such desperate need for food? There is no reason, of course.
>
> "But there is a need for telling people who are hungry or who are starving just where food can be obtained. There is a need to bring food from the farm to the storage facility, from the storage facility to the processing center, from the processing center to distribution points. Marketing is roads, and railways, and ports and harbors. Marketing is communications, and trucks, and boats, and warehouses and storage bins, and collection points and distribution centers, and so on. Marketing is all of these things right down to the consideration of packaging and handling . . ."

> . . . from conference proceedings, 1969

By the time the first five years of conferences concluded the world was well on its way toward the alleviation of hunger. The problem was not fully resolved, but considerably improved. Now was introduced a new phase around which to structure future agendas. The many complexities that modern society had developed in its progression had been considered and analyzed, and many innovations had been successfully introduced.

The one major, incontrovertible success had been the development of universal awareness. That awareness had been fostered by many factors, and was now worldwide. Food was now in more bellies and on more minds that it had ever been before.

But the conference was not only about food, as we can see. It also represented a forerunner of a new kind of corporate thinking. A change in the corporate molecule, as we have called it. This thinking recognizes that the basic structure of a corporation can re-form around the nucleus of a new idea and, while it continues to do the same things, it does them better and with a different viewpoint, a different purpose. By changing the goal and not the processes, the entire function and effect of corporate thrust in a given area can change, and with it, change the force and direction of an entire industry.

The corporation, like the series of conferences, had successfully concluded what was now referred to as Phase I, and was ready to undertake Phase II.

The food production knot had been untied. The tangled distribution knot lay ahead. It was less basic, more complex. But success likes a challenge, and the conferences continued.

continued commitment

By 1970 the worldwide trend of continued shortages had been largely overcome. Thanks largely to the "Green Revolution," hope was very much in the ascendancy. The possibility of success had become realistic. People everywhere now talked as though it was actually possible to raise enough food for the people of the earth; likewise more attention was being paid to those who spoke at the World Food Production Conferences.

At the sixth annual conference, panelists included both government agricultural ministers and bankers. The observers included representatives from the UNFAO, from educational institutions, from private charities active in providing food for the hungry, as well as representatives of both government agencies and of governments themselves.

This recognition of the conferences as a sparking wheel for increasing world food supplies was unmistakable. They had achieved a hard-won credibility and were taking attention away from the doomsayers who continued to develop new vocabularies and formulate new ideas that seemed designed to terrorize the world into inaction. The conferences, on the other hand, were no longer just a call to action . . . they represented action itself.

The Sixth Asia/Pacific Conference, held in Manila, was warmly greeted by the President of the Republic of the Philippines, who even suggested a point for its agenda:

> "Asian nations have inched closer towards each other in such diverse projects as the Asian Development Bank, the Asian and Pacific Council, and the Association of Southeast Asian Nations.

"Perhaps it is in these alliances that we may find the instrument that could carry out the program for an exchange of information on improving food production.

"This is one item that you would do well to take up during this conference. I assure you that whatever the consensus of your conference is in this matter it will enjoy the support of my government . . ."

. . . from conference proceedings, 1970

Also attending the Sixth World Food Production Conference was Dr. Robert Chandler, Director of the International Rice Research Institute and the man who, with another conference participant, Dr. Norman Borlaug, is largely credited for the success of the Green Revolution. It was IRRI which had developed both the farming technology and the economic procedures that led to Masagana 99 (see Chapter 10). He spoke of the promise of research:

". . . The vistas for future research are wide and full of promise, if man will control his own reproduction and will develop the production of food crops to the maximum. Agronomists at the Institute have produced 23,000 kilograms per hectare of rice in 12 months on the same land. By multiple cropping, they have grown a crop of rice, another of sweet corn, a third of sweet potatoes, and a fourth of soybeans—all in one year.

"With new varieties possessing the ability to respond well to modern methods of crop production, the future will see an unprecedented use of agricultural chemicals, particularly fertilizers, insecticides and pesticides. Commercial companies will play an indispensable role in the great upsurge of food production by providing new and better chemicals at the lowest possible costs."

. . . from conference proceedings, 1970

Both conference reports and other indications seemed to point toward a massing of action along the food production front. A war on hunger was taking place. It was still only unofficially declared in forums like the World Food Production Conferences, but it was real nonetheless. And action invariably produced results. If nothing else, it often generated further action, and the continuing stimulation of layer after layer of process and procedure was vitally important to the future of food. To produce more food, the world needed research, farmer education, farmer credit, and the means of transferring technology and input to the farmer. That was action. That was result . . . and that was the conferences.

Exactly what direct effect conference proceedings were having on the surge of agriculture, neither the sponsors nor conferees ever tried to gauge, for it was impossible to measure. They found it sufficient to know that they were part of a great success, and took that to mean that whatever they were doing was being done right.

Action was reported by many at the sixth conference. A brief report by the Managing Director of a major Japanese firm showed one way in which the conferences, their concerns and conferees, had played a role in progress. After five years of exchanging information and developing relationships, it was not surprising to hear:

"Technical cooperation on a government-to-government basis is, I am sure, beneficial to our industry as well as to the economic development of the recipient country. And, no doubt, farmers in these countries will realize the benefits of using fertilizers. However, as long as these activities are carried out through experiment stations and training centers, the effect is rather indirect. Furthermore, even when farmers realize the advantages of adopting these new methods, they are often helpless to do so because of a lack of capital or credit.

"An outstanding example of a program that breaks through these economic bottlenecks is the Bimas Project, in Indonesia. This project, conceived by our colleague, Mr. Sadikin, is a unique situation where the Indonesian government is actively, positively, and directly involved in increased food production by providing farmers with the necessary inputs and technical guidance to produce more rice . . .

"I am happy to say that my company participates in this program. We currently have 14 agricultural experts working in West Java and Sumatra, together with nearly 30 Indonesian agricultural workers on some 225,000 hectares of rice fields.

"We supply agricultural chemicals, power sprayers, hand sprayers, Jeeps, motorcycles, bicycles, and maintenance, plus technical assistance. The total cost for the project is more than $7 million. Indonesia's economy is improving year by year, and I have no doubt that these projects have been playing an important role in stabilizing the people's livelihood. Through united efforts like these, 'Freedom from Hunger' can become a reality in the Asia/Pacific area."

. . . from conference proceedings, 1970

Huge successes, like that of the Green Revolution, are made up of many very small parts, each contributing something that nothing else can, each a link in the chain of distribution, or nutrition, or some other subdivision of progress. Not everything good accomplished was large, nor was everything a product of tomorrow's science today; some of the very human and important contributions to the feeding of the world were very small, considering the immensity of the problem, but loomed very large in the lives of those who needed, and then *had*, the benefit of help.

One such example resulted from looking back through the agricultural history of one of the developed nations. Something that had once helped its small farmers, it was reasoned, might again make a contribution to someone else on the way up. So, with this practical interest in nostalgia, something *was* found and resurrected from the attic of agriculture. It was something that could be implemented quickly and inexpensively, and it moved conference concern outside the narrow range of food production, into the area of food supply. It was something that could help people eat and was readily available, so it was discussed at the conference. It meant action, all right—not pie-in-the-sky, but canned food on the shelf:

"A partial solution has already proved effective in providing more continuity to life. It seeks an end to the feast or famine cycle through the use of common glass jars. I am referring to the Community Canning Centers. This tested program directly attacks the problem of seasonal availability of food by preserving excess production.

"Community Canning Centers were designed about 45 years

ago by Ball Brothers—a U.S. pioneer in the home canning industry. Today these centers are being successfully operated in many economically underdeveloped areas of the world. The centers contain the basic equipment needed to properly preserve food on a local community-wide basis. One such center can serve 500 to 2,000 families, by allowing them to put aside farm produce during the harvest season—the time of plenty—to improve their diet on a year-round basis.

An investment of $6,000 to $8,000 will provide all the necessary equipment—plus the technical assistance—to preserve perishable foods. The equipment can be housed in almost any existing structure. The result is that food—whether vegetables, fruit, meat or fish—is made safe for the famine season. It is an effective attack on the tragedy of food spoilage . . .

"Community Canning Centers offer at least a cooperative first step toward establishing the 'continuity of life.' They provide, at low cost, a simple method for preserving and storing foods. Above all, the centers help families make a direct and positive contribution to the quality and course of their own lives."

. . . from conference proceedings, 1970

Now that more food was being grown, the possibility of an adequate food supply had been demonstrated. That was, it seemed in retrospect, the easy part, the first step only.

Now the steps would get more complex. A crop was not, by itself, a guarantee against hunger. On a small scale, the canning centers were helping. But it was not that simple a matter. There is more to agriculture than the growing of food, as the president of the Asian Development Bank made clear:

". . . Agricultural development may be compared to a giant chain; one missing link and there is no development. Building a dam while, at the same time, an extension worker remains uninformed about his role in bringing this new technology to the individual farmer, means only that a dam has been built.

"If we had not known this before, the results of our Asian Agricultural Survey would surely have warned us of the countless interlinked problems that must be overcome before agricultural development can be achieved.

"Our work will make headlines in few newspapers, but when

a country realizes self-sufficiency in rice production for the first time in a century, we can know that we have helped make this possible.

"New strains of rice and wheat bring the promise, for the first time, of an abundance of food. But new rice is a development in agriculture, not agricultural development. It is one link in the giant chain.

"With the new technology comes new hope—and new problems. Fields must be better irrigated than ever before; fields must be better fertilized than ever before; water management must be practiced with a sophistication never before achieved; agricultural credit banks must be effectively organized; extension workers trained; a market organized.

"Details, but important details. Vital details . . .

". . . It is hard to envisage a time when the Asian Development Bank will not be engaged in agricultural development. For, as I mentioned earlier, the new technology in agriculture does not solve the problems of food production and agricultural development. Technology is a means, not an end. And though we now have the means to end hunger in Asia, a host of new and more sophisticated problems have arisen.

"How, for instance, is the increasing requirement for agricultural credit to be handled? How is it to be channeled to the smaller, or subsistence farmer?

"Which countries must push toward rapid diversification of crops? Mindful of the fact that the demand for rice may soon fall behind supply, which among alternate crops should be first considered?

"Who shall take the lead for new approaches to marketing? At what level should price supports for various crops be fixed? What priority should be placed on the establishment of commodity exchanges? Of storage facilities?

"These are but a few of the questions to which we must now address ourselves. The questions are difficult; more difficult still are the answers . . .

"Agricultural development in Asia has now gathered, for perhaps the first time, a momentum of its own. That momentum must be continued, and not allowed to stagnate . . .

"The Asian Development Bank will continue to play its part in the agricultural development of the member countries of our region. We stand ready to offer assistance to both the public and

private sectors in bringing about a more prosperous future for Asia. "

. . . from conference proceedings, 1970

The original principle of providing an atmosphere for honest and frank discussion never left the conferences. There was never a restriction imposed on subject matter that might be brought before a conference by conferees, so long as that matter had a reasonably direct bearing on the fight against hunger.

That the causes of hunger are many and varied none can doubt. Each cause deserves analysis and the formulation of planning that could lead to its removal. But food, itself, was not a *cause* of hunger; it was a *cure*.

So that remained the major immediate concern of the conferences. Food, and the means of increasingly providing more of it, were, moreover, within the particular expertise of the conferees. Fortunately, the value of this unique gathering was becoming increasingly understood by more and more people with influence and responsibility in the feeding of nations. Support for effort is a valuable assistant to progress, and was always gladly received at conferences, especially support that promised action toward solving the basic problem:

"*. . . I would like to reiterate my strong endorsement of holding conferences like this, as they provide us with insight into the progress and advances made by member countries for possible adoption and implementation by the other members. It is only through cooperative effort such as this that we will be able to attain economic advancement in this area.*

"*At this juncture, allow me to congratulate both the International Minerals and Chemical Corporation, which sponsored these annual conferences, and the participating countries for their dedication in assuming the role of leaders in the development of agriculture, particularly in the developing nations.*

"*As Secretary of Agriculture and Natural Resources, and as Vice President of the Philippines, I wish to pledge to you my wholehearted cooperation now and in the future, to the end that together we shall attain not only the advancement of our mutual economic well-*

being, but also the peace and contentment that necessarily go with economic prosperity."

. . . from conference proceedings, 1970

Sometimes encouragement for continued commitment came in less direct ways. Often it was found in a conference report of past action, taken from an analysis of figures indicating improved yields and increased fertilization. There is one example from the Latin American Food Production Conference where such encouragement was found in a description of food production progress that pointed right at the heart of the matter:

"During the last ten years, the decade of the 60s, agricultural production in Mexico increased at an average annual rate of over four percent. The government of Mexico has played a leading role in achieving these results through enlightened policies that have encouraged the rapid development of the agricultural sector at all levels . . .

"The Department of Agriculture and Cattle has declared that among those factors which have contributed the most to the success of agricultural development programs, the constant and increased use of fertilizers has made the greatest contribution to expanded agricultural productivity. Thus, it is recognized and accepted, both in the field and in official circles, that fertilizers are playing an important role in Mexico's increased food production. This increased production has placed us in a food surplus position for the first time in many, many years, despite our ever-increasing population.

"It is peculiar to our agriculture that, when a particular technical advance is seen, it introduces a veritable chain reaction. For instance, lands benefitting from irrigation works show the rapid introduction and multiplication of other improved technology, such as more and better technical services, more agricultural machinery and, above all, a greater volume of fertilizers, with improved seeds and pesticides. The introduction of fertilizers, too, has served as a catalyst of agricultural development, bringing with it the adoption of other improved technology and the resulting increases in production."

. . . from conference proceedings, 1970

And sometimes encouragement came from the mere expression of a hope . . . a hope that seemed about to be realized, and one that showed the quality of understanding the conferences were always working for, the quality that had success built into it:

> *"The Argentine government considers it absolutely necessary that our country increase its agricultural production—both to achieve self-sufficiency in food production and to improve our foreign trade position. Since we do not have additional lands to bring into production, this means we must increase our present yields. And yield increases will necessitate increased fertilization, since this is the only important technological factor our extensive agriculture has not yet incorporated.*
>
> *". . . The success of such a program, based on a total of over 60 million hectares, could provide a barrier to hunger for years to come. Even a slight increase in yields would be of such a magnitude that it would more than pay for the cost of such a program."*

> *. . . from conference proceedings, 1970*

By the time of the middle conference years, there was no doubt that progress had been, and was being, made. Though with the increases in food production which proved, really, to have been the simplest step, there came additional concerns. With food production up, these concerns came swiftly and surely, and loomed large behind the overall problem of providing more food for more people.

The conferences continued to serve as a clearing house for activity—and even for non-activity. Where something was lagging in the overall food situation, it was necessary to point it out, discuss it, and seek means to correct it. While this was not simple, it was not beyond the reach of the conference. It, too, could be accomplished. But, as the conference chairman pointed out, it would not be easy:

> *"Man is winning the struggle against hunger and starvation throughout much of the world, but complex problems remain, problems which threaten to curtail progress in this critical area of food production if we do not act at once to solve them. We have found that*

countries often face new hurdles to development as they move from food-deficient to food-surplus conditions. And some of these problems may be even more complex than the earlier challenge of merely growing more food. We must work together to encourage public and private sectors to share the responsibility for solving these new 'problems of success.' In the months and years ahead, all segments of a nation's economy—from government and educational bodies to financial institutions and agricultural suppliers—must combine their skills in an all-out effort that will place recent achievements on a solid foundation for dramatic future development. It cannot be accomplished with anything less than total effort."

. . . from conference proceedings, 1971

Nor was hunger to be completely separated from other world problems. The conferences had commanded so much worldwide attention and interest that new inputs were being received from unexpected sources. They came from those whose interests extended beyond agriculture, and who came to share with the conferees concerns they saw as important elements in the overall problem of hunger. Neither hunger nor agriculture could remain entirely apart from other aspects of the complex human situation.

In his opening remarks to the Asia/Pacific Food Production Conference, held in India, the President of the International Chamber of Commerce provided insight into the "problem behind the problem":

". . . The war on hunger cannot truly be won unless agriculture as a whole prospers, and the activities of industry and agriculture are mutually reinforcing.

"In developing countries traditional agricultural operations are being gradually transformed, thanks to research and development. Scientists and plant breeders have established, by the principle of adaptive research, that it should be possible to increase yield and improve nutritive quality. The 'Green Revolution' has aroused interest, as well as hope among the teeming millions of the world. But, along with this, new problems have come up. The very circumstances which have made it possible for plenty to appear on the horizon have also given rise to new and more complicated factors.

Apart from the imbalances and disparaties in the pace of develop-ment, there is the realization that greater food production by itself is not enough. The vast masses of the rural community, the landless peasants, are now exposed to mass-communication media, and see the growth of affluence and seek a share of it . . ."

. . . from conference proceedings, 1971

But hope continued to press forward at the conferences. All past success had been based on hope . . . hope expressed in action. That was, perhaps, foremost among the principles of success. The conferences could not ameliorate man's problems alone, but they could spark activity and concern, and focus attention on basic concerns—information and enthusiasm de-signed to increase food production. That was fundamental. That was secure. Only then could the conferences broaden their efforts and begin dealing with the increasing complexity of the problem.

It took time, during the middle conference years, to reex-amine what ground had already been covered. From that per-spective would emerge the next phase of activity. An occasional look back was necessary, and important, as in this instance:

"We can recall times when our deliberations were held in the shadow of crop failures and crises. We have only to think back as far as 1966 to a time when the monsoon rains of India did not come. As a result, 60 million lives were placed in jeopardy.

"Today, we are together at a time when we may share a greater optimism than has ever before been warranted.

"Everywhere there is a special kind of animation. Some call it the spirit of possibility . . . Certainly, it is easy to find in it fresh encouragement for our efforts.

"Answers which were a generation in the making in the labora-tories are suddenly upon us, in the foreground of agricultural think-ing and planning.

"The Green Revolution, in country after country, is having its miracle effects. Harvests spring four-fold, ten-fold, sixteen-fold.

"New strains of cereals are remarkably independent of seasonal and geographical differences. Planting may now be made over a wide span of time, and a wider geographic area. Moreover, maturity

is faster. One type of rice, for instance, is ready for harvest in four months, instead of the usual five to six months.

"All this opens the way to multiple cropping in tropical and sub-tropical regions where the supply of water is adequate. Under favorable conditions even four crops a year are not unheard of . . ."

. . . from conference proceedings, 1971

From the very beginning, the world press had followed closely the development of IMC's World Food Production Conferences. Each meeting had resulted in comprehensive coverage and attention by the news media, including newspapers, magazines, radio and television.

But none could compare with the interest and exposure given the conference after its fifth year. The Sixth Asia/Pacific Food Production Conference, held in Manila in March of 1970, was widely reported not only in the Philippines, where it had been addressed by the President of the nation, but throughout the Asia/Pacific area of the globe. There were feature stories on the conference itself, special articles about conference exhibits, and stories on conference proceedings and activities, as well as special coverage of numerous conferees in their own countries.

The same enthusiastic attention was given to the Latin American Conference held a month later in Chile. It seemed there was a great, emerging understanding of the role of the conferences in the feeding of the hungry. Where there was much hunger—typically where many could not read the papers or see the television—there was special emphasis to those whom the media did reach touching on the burdens they shared with their countrymen, and on the hope of progress so far.

There was also wide press attention given to hope for the future, as this conference explored and brought to light new opportunities for feeding people and increasing their general welfare. This would occur through raising the overall benefit level of agriculture, and so help produce more farmer income and generate more favorable balance of trade with other nations. Many new and valuable ideas kept coming forward at the conference, and were made practical by explanation and by example:

*"Any nation that ignores the full potential of its inland water re-
sources as a means of supporting high-protein fish farming is missing
a good opportunity in its fight against hunger and malnutrition.
Korea is working aggressively to take full advantage of this aspect
of the food production picture, and promises to achieve significant
gains in fish farming in the years ahead."*

. . . *from conference proceedings, 1971*

Food, and the possibility for increasing its production, continued to dance in a mesmerizing fashion before the eyes of
the world. The more it seemed possible to increasing numbers
of people to raise enough food for the world's population, the
more valued the idea became. Where once some intellectuals of
developed nations were bemused by the numbers relating to
populations, and developing philosophical attitudes to make
hunger something that had to be lived with, now there was hope
in the streets, and other intellectuals everywhere—especially
those with a positive understanding of business methods and
techniques—could see the brightened possibilities . . . not only
for increased food production, but for spreading the variety of
goods and services required all along the food routes from
growth to consumption.

No matter the range of subject matter undertaken at the
conferences, they always kept to a practical agenda. The conferences were not, after all, about hope; each was a conference
on food production. They were seen, by those present and
many others, as a vital part of agricultural progress. In a special
message to the conference of 1971, India's President Giri said,
"The future well-being of mankind needs greater emphasis on
the production of food, without which all efforts for economic
development and progress will bear no fruit."

Food production remained, of course, the major concern of
the conferees. If there was any result to be determined from
their efforts it was, ultimately, to be measured in increases in
the production of food. There was reason for optimism, because
progress had been recorded. But there was also reason for despair, because the results had not yet overcome the problem.
There were still millions dying every year from eating too little.
Malnutrition and hunger-related diseases still stalked the help-

less members of the human species who remained outside the circles of progress which measured success.

With all the success of the conferences in commanding the attention of concerned agencies and individuals, and with all the success of the "Green Revolution" that was so widely spoken of in those days, the conferences continued determinedly along the relatively narrow path of increasing food production still further. That there would be many other considerations required to resolve the many imbalances and injustices that centuries of civilized living had produced, was understood. But the conferences determined that their role was to hew to the situation of *now*, to the means of adding food to the tables of the world's hungry. Food was perceived as first in the chain of developing progress, and it was within the purview of the conferences to do something about food. To continue to do so they needed periodic clarification of direction, of role, and of their responsibility.

In his keynote address to the Eighth Latin American Food Production Conference, Sidney Keel, IMC Vice President and Conference Chairman, restated the realistic new optimism:

> ". . . The biggest problem we face today, of course, is that of world hunger. And this meeting underlines the fact that to solve the problem of world hunger, we need the total combined efforts of both private industry and public government . . . and attests that we in private industry recognize this responsibility.
>
> "There's still one more way that we differ from other groups approaching the problem of world hunger. Even the most optimistic sociologists cannot see the possibility of arresting population growth for at least several decades. But we here know that we already possess the technology to answer the problem of world hunger . . . not only today but for those several decades to come. The decades the world needs to answer the problem of population growth itself . . ."

> . . . from conference proceedings, 1972

Those assembled did, indeed, know that man possessed the technology needed to answer the problem of world hunger. That there were other problems within the basic problem was also known to the conferees. They were still discussing how to best resolve those problems and to pass that working knowledge on to the world. They were still learning, too, of their success in that activity.

One of the acts of an early conference had been to conduct a study of rural credit practices in Latin America. Now, at the Eighth Conference, one of the conferees reported:

> *"Whereas in 1964 only the Central Bank of Brazil and a few official State Banks were working with farm loans, now 185 financial institutions are active in this area. And the government has assured the flow of loans for not only farm production, but for objectives correlated to farm production which indirectly will determine its success. . . .*
>
> *"We are confident that all of the projects encompassed in Brazil's rural credit policy will eventually enable the country to increase the production of farm and livestock products for export, thus assuring the additional foreign exchange necessary to maintain the growth of our economy."*
>
> *. . . from conference proceedings, 1972*

The growth of the economy is an important—even though secondary—part of agriculture's role. The American Ambassador to Japan addressed delegates in Tokyo prior to the conference in Korea, in 1972, in this regard:

> *"The agricultural business sector's contributions to solving the world's food problems have been immense. You are obviously aware that the problem is not simply one of developing better fertilizers, seeds, and equipment, and distributing them more wisely. As you have noted, efforts must also be made to develop better transportation, storage and distribution systems; to encourage positive government policies; to overcome farmers' reluctance to adopt new and more efficient agricultural methods; and to answer the questions on the environmental impact of agricultural chemicals.*
>
> *"These problems are international in scope and their solution requires international cooperation and coordination. Your conferences for the past eight years have provided a very useful and productive forum for discussion of the international implications of these problems.*
>
> *"I assume some of you also took part in IMC's Second Asia/*

Pacific Food Production Conference which was held in Tokyo in 1966.

"The world food situation that year was much less promising than today for several reasons. The much-heralded Green Revolution had not yet begun. A growing disparity between population and food productivity threatened millions of human beings in less-developed lands. Political forces often hampered economical and efficient movement of foodstuffs from food-surplus nations to food-deficient nations. To many experts, the situation was touch-and-go, with the outcome very much in doubt.

"This year's conference will focus attention on problem areas, to . . . but what a difference in scope!"

The difference in scope was, indeed, noticeable. This conference now was deep into discussion of cooperation between each of the varied elements relating to agriculture. Specifically, the group was concerned with the relationship of continued increase in food production to the governments of various nations. Some governments were growing concerned about real and potential ecological and pollution problems. That some of these problems were real was hardly in dispute. How to approach them was, however, the subject of much passionate discussion.

As to the role of the government in such concerns, a conferee from Singapore spoke eloquently:

"Our government, in formulating its development plans, has to balance its programs against the potential dangers from pollution in both the industrial and agricultural areas. While it would like to remain totally free from some of the threats of serious pollution, Malaysian government officials appear to recognize that the critical needs of any developing country may force compromises. Actions may be required to allow certain operations which may impose some disruption of the environment, but which offer needed opportunities for national growth and expansion in world trade, while striving to provide adequate food supplies for the country's people.

"The greatest pollution threat in Asia has been that of malnutrition and the low quality of life. Reduce this form of pollution to the stage where more fashionable forms of pollution become the

menace, and hundreds of millions of people would regard it as a fair exchange. Meanwhile, it is vital to work within a given country's own set of values and circumstances to achieve those goals most sought after by its own people.

"To that end, close cooperation between public and private sectors is paramount."

. . . from conference proceedings, 1972

By the time of the Ninth Conference, in 1973, the problems had shifted somewhat. Severe weather and the Russian purchase of wheat had driven scarce food prices up higher, and fertilizers were more expensive and scarce, as well. The keynote address that year clearly outlined the situation:

"In our early conferences, there was great emphasis on increasing production by massive use of fertilizers, without major regard to inputs such as seeds, cultivation practices, losses after harvest and in storage, the distribution and marketing infrastructure, and the like. Then need was so great, and the response from fertilizer could be so dramatic, that our emphasis was almost unilateral in favor of more and more fertilizer.

"As the years progressed, we began to see tangible results from such actions. Total world food production began to increase. Where the per capita food production of the six major countries in South America, for example, had been declining, we had finally reversed that trend in two of the six nations and had raised it appreciably in two of the others. India and Pakistan had raised total food production dramatically. Per capita increases also showed up in Thailand, Malaysia, Korea, Taiwan, and Ceylon. There really could be said to have been significant progress throughout the world—and it could be further said that some of this progress resulted from our own World Food Production Conferences and similar activities.

"But now, suddenly, we find ourselves in a changed world, in a world of shortages where just yesterday there were surpluses. Many factors occurring simultaneously had a converging and reinforcing effect on each other—the sale of huge quantities of U.S. grain to Russia and China, Canadian strikes and governmental regulations, severe weather in almost every sector of the globe, the unexplained

shifting of ocean currents off Peru that caused a reduction in the
catch of fish and, hence, in the availability of fishmeal protein—all of
these things conspired to turn our world completely around . . ."

. . . from conference proceedings, 1973

With the world of food supply so "turned around," it became incumbent on the conference to consider other aspects of food besides production. Weather had held back production, not technology; and this, as yet, agriculture could do little about. But the immediate situation did mean that more attention would need to be paid to protecting food after harvest so that its value was not wasted. This is a much bigger problem than is commonly realized, and it was called forcefully to the attention of the conferees:

"There is no question that food losses to insects, rodents, and molds
reaches staggering amounts in volume as well as value. While the
estimates vary, it is generally agreed that one-fifth to one-third of
what agriculture is producing never reaches the consumer. In many
hungry nations this loss often exceeds 50 percent, and in extreme
cases such losses have been total!

"Moderate estimates, says the FAO, indicate that the destruction
of food by rodents, insects, birds, and molds, while it is in storage
and in transit to the consumer, robs hundreds of millions of people
of at least one-fifth of the food they might be eating . . ."

. . . from conference proceedings, 1973

The concern for food had now encompassed a great many other concerns. In the more developed nations, some of these concerns blew back and forth with each wind; but where the hunger for food and nutrition had gnawed steadily from one generation to the next for a thousand years, the concern was fixed. It was food. Hunger for food came first. When that had been taken care of, there would be time enough to go on to other things.

Much had happened to bring about this shifting of attention from the causes of the most widespread human misery to other concerns. It was no longer the same world . . . now food was not just *talk*, but had become *grain*. In many places it was now home-owned grain, not imported grain, not grain bought on the international market, but grain of the people of a nation that had raised it themselves, on their own poor land.

When something is made to appear practically on command, that never appeared before, it is called magic. And it happened. As the world watched, the once near-barren paddies and fields focused their power to produce and turned the whole country-side, the whole world . . . green! It was a magic of logic, science, and persistence. It grew from the work done by the people of the International Rice Research Institute under the direction of Dr. Robert Chandler, who had conducted fellow conferees through the Institute at Los Banos, and by the people of the International Wheat and Maize Institute in Mexico, under the direction of Nobel Peace Prize winner Dr. Norman Borlaug.

In Dr. Borlaug's talk to his fellow conferees at the Ninth Latin American Food Production Conference, he touched on many of the concerns that had spotlighted the later confer-ences, as well as on the hope whose rays had already penetrated much gloom. His eloquence combined so well with the science and humanity that *are* the man, that excerpts from his address provide the captions for a picture story of the miracle itself: the Green Revolution with which Dr. Borlaug is so closely identified.

the green revolution

*The material in this chapter
is excerpted from an address by
Dr. Norman Borlaug to
the Latin American Food Production Conference
at El Salvador in 1973*

While I'm speaking, world population will add another 2,000 people . . . that will take about 15 minutes . . . at the outside. For the past two days we've been talking about the increasing food problem. Most of the conversation has hinged on the one most important ingredient of all—fertilizer.

It's only with the proper use of fertilizer that we can hope to continue to meet the growing food demands of the world. A world that, with a few exceptions, is running out of arable land. Brazil still has vast tracts of land that can be brought under cultivation, but there are few other countries with this potential. So what we have to do, always, is to try to make each acre of land produce much more than it has ever produced before. And, I think that with the introduction of new scientific discoveries and new technologies, this is being done.

There are those who say that the land is wearing out, that we are depleting our resources, and even—in certain places—abusing them. But I would like to point to the other side of the picture.

I grew up on a very small farm, in the very northeastern corner of Iowa. Nearby was a small tract of land, a half-section of virgin prairie. And when I go and stand in the center of this tract of land in mid-summer it's not very impressive—it's the way it was when the pioneers came. And, it's especially not impressive when I look to one side and see beautiful fields of clover or alfalfa, and to another side and see 100-bushel corn, or 35-bushel soybeans.

If you look back a bit farther into the history of the five major cornbelt states in the U.S.A., you'll see that in the mid 1880s the average yield in those states was 25-26 bushels of corn per acre. Today, it stands at 100. Have we destroyed the fertility, or have we improved the fertility? Obviously, it isn't just the soil fertility that's involved. We have learned how to prepare the land better, how to control the weeds and the pests, and we have improved seeds to go along with the better use of plant nutrients.

All of these together have made these tremendous changes, and it's the only way we could feed the population of the world today. But we have a tremendous job ahead of us.

In 1971, there was an all-time record of cereal grains produced in the world—1,106,000,000 metric tons. Now, in the developing countries a large part of these grains are consumed directly, because there isn't enough grain so they can afford to convert it to meat products.

Chicken takes 3 pounds of grain for each pound of meat; or 5 to 6 in the case of ham and pork; or 8 to 9 in the case of beef.

So the people in these countries must eat the cereals direct, whether it be rice, or wheat, or combinations; and then supplement their diets with legumes or kidney beans, if it's in a corn or maize diet or, in India or Pakistan, it will generally be lentils or pigeon peas.

But let's go back to this figure—this record crop—of 1,106,000,000 tons. Visualize it as a highway built of grain, that goes around the earth at the Equator, 18-1/2 meters wide and 2 meters deep. That's what that all-time record crop of 1971 represented. It's quite a pile of grain, expressed that way.

But we are growing; the population of the world is growing by 76 million more people each year. This means that just to stand still . . . to produce the same per capita supply of grain . . . we have to produce an additional 27 million tons every year. That means we have to start building a new highway of grain around the earth at the rate of 1,000 kilometers, or roughly 600 miles, each and every year. But last year we didn't complete the original highway. World production, because of droughts, went down by 42 million tons, but population growth kept going up and up. And so, in these

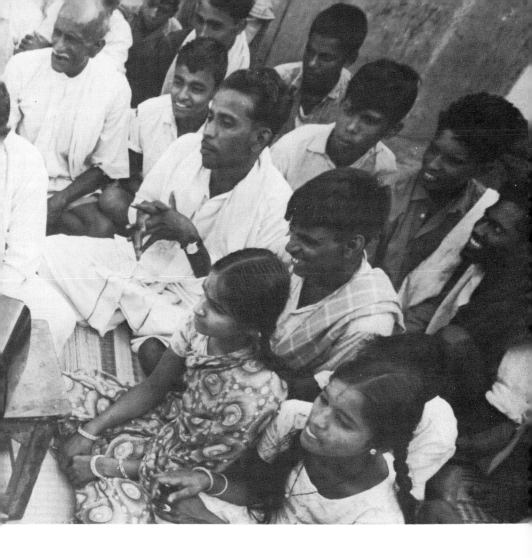

last two years, when we should have built these 2,000 kilometers on the new highway, we will have built, if the estimates are right, only 300 kilometers. So, we have fallen behind.

Then why didn't more people starve? The reason, of course, is that we're living out of our reserve stocks. These stocks have dropped something on the order of 40 million metric tons of food grains during the past year. And, if something happens in the next two or three years, and these stocks are not replenished, there could be 50 to 200 million people who would face death from famine.

People say the situation isn't so bad, because reserves were just as low 20 years ago. But, we now number 1,100,000,000 more people than we did 20 years ago. So, to compare those reserves with the reserves of today is meaningless. That's the situation we are up against.

If we look at the most important ingredient in increasing food production, it comes back to fertilizer. To produce the 27 million metric tons of grain that we need to add each year, we are conservatively estimating that we will need to produce 2,700,000 more tons of nitrogen . . . half that much of phosphate and, perhaps, one-third that much of potash each year. All that just to hold the line.

We aren't going to correct these things overnight, and we're all in this trouble together. Whether you work from the standpoint of trying to grow the plants, or produce the fertilizer, or finance all of these new investments, it's all part and parcel of the same picture.

Now, how could we have gotten into this trouble? I think that we've been carrying inadequate reserves to take care of a bad year. This year we've seen that what were thought to be adequate reserves just weren't adequate. Though anyone who sat down and looked at the figures couldn't help but be aware that there had to be some other kind of a reserve to back up the one that has been provided by the grain exporting nations since the end of World War II.

These nations served as warehousers, brokers, and bankers for the effective grain reserve over that period of 28 years, and world grain and food prices were surprisingly stable because of this cushion, or buffer. But once these reserves were depleted by the events of the past year-and-a-half, everything was thrown out of equilibrium, and prices skyrocketed. And it doesn't make any difference whether you're talking about bread or about meat—it's all a part of the same problem.

As incomes go up, people eat more animal products. Several pounds of grain are needed for conversion into each pound of meat, cheese, eggs, or whatever the substance is. This is a luxury and, as we get more crowded in this world, we are going to have to find ways to balance diets by building and designing new forms and varieties of grains; and at the same time improve the production of beans, chickpeas, and other supplements needed to balance cereal diets.

These are things that have been neglected. In the case of improving diets, or improving the nutritive value of cereals, the know-how has just been opening up—over the last 8 or 9 years in the case of maize, within the last 3 years in the case of barley, and within the past few months for sorghum. Curiously enough, we haven't found that we can manipulate genetics in the two major staple foods, rice and wheat. We have to look more . . . and we have to look fast.

But let's not be pessimistic. When we look at what the world has built in 12,000 years, great things have been achieved. And they were not achieved by pessimists. Had the naked apes, our ancestors, been pessimistic when they had a rock in one hand, a club in the other, and an empty stomach, they'd never have made the grade, and we wouldn't be here discussing the problems we face today.

So, I have faith in the future if we organize ourselves, and I think that one thing we must all do is not to pass negativism on to our sons and daughters. For that is a poison that's worse than any other.

masagana 99

The World Food Production Conferences were dedicated to the belief that man possessed the knowledge and ability to produce enough food for everyone. Their proceedings clearly suggested that if cooperation could be developed between the varied agricultural disciplines, the world could be transformed quickly into a broad, round garden, growing everything required by its inhabitants. That was a nice dream, some thought, but well beyond realization. Determining the difference between a dream and a workable idea was one of the functions of the conference.

One significant contribution of the conference participants was identification of the varied strings that needed to be pulled in proper sequence to move the many-jointed marionette of agriculture forward in traditionally slow-moving farm areas.

Many of these individual strings had already been identified and were well known: Availability of new plant varieties with a high-yield potential; availability of fertilizer required to help the new varieties reach optimum yield; availability of irrigation; knowledge of how to work with the new technology; and, perhaps above all, the need for farmer education and credit. It had been stressed again and again: Government cooperation was an imperative; credit availability was an imperative; and farmer education was an imperative. In addition, sound counsel from trained field technicians had to be available. Where these requirements were met, food production could be increased.

At the Tenth World Food Production Conference, one guest speaker offered a special report which proved an exciting demonstration of just what could happen when those requirements *were* met.

As the report began to unfold, the conferees witnessed a vindication of their ideas, of their beliefs in the potential for man to increase his food production by mighty leaps. They knew with certainty that, if man once set his mind to it and stopped parroting the doom forecast by Malthus, it could be done swiftly.

In the growing season of 1971-72, an experiment was begun.

By the time it worked its way across the entire Philippines it had produced such a resounding rice harvest that the question of possibility was forever laid to rest. It *could* be done, and the story of "Masagana 99" provided some conclusive evidence. For the report documented that, in the space of a single growing season, the Philippines obtained record rice harvests, and more individual farmers gained greater prosperity than ever before. In 1973-74, the Philippines recorded a 28 percent increase over the preceeding year. How this came to happen is an exciting story.

It began with a bright ray of hope in an otherwise dark climate . . . the work being done by the International Rice Research Institute at Los Banos. There, cooperating with the University of the Philippines, the IRRI carried out tests on its latest high-yield variety of rice. This new variety was being tested under actual farm conditions and was carefully monitored. Tests were also being conducted on 150 farm plots scattered about the island of Luzon.

IRRI had, as early as 1965 (the same year the First World Food Production Conference was held), demonstrated that as much as eight tons of rice per hectare could be taken from irrigated land using newly developed high-yielding varieties. Before Masagana 99 got underway, IRRI research had produced rice varieties that could—under ideal conditions and care—turn out as much as 11 tons. On farmers' fields they produced four and five tons per hectare. As a comparison, the average yield on a Philippine farm at the time was one ton per hectare; the obvious advantage was spectacular.

That was about the only ray of hope in Philippine agriculture at that moment. During the crop year 1970-71 there had been 28 typhoons within a six-month period. The rice harvest advanced only 2 percent over the previous year and, at 5.3 million metric tons, was well below the amount needed by the nation to feed its own people.

The following year, Philippine rice farmers were hit hard by a serious epidemic of Tungro—a virus carried by the green leafhopper that withers the rice plant before the grains can form. Rice production that year dropped to 5.1 million metric tons.

In the growing season of 1972-73, just after the main crop was transplanted, the major rice producing area of Central Luzon was flooded, end-to-end, by three-and-a-half weeks of constant rain. It was reported that in many places water levels rose to the rooftops of the farmers' homes. That year, production of rice dropped to 4.4 million tons.

This series of disasters took place in the face of a continuing rise in population with its consequent consumption requirements. The world market for rice was facing corresponding shortages and the Philippine government realized that, if its people were to eat, the farmers had to contrive a massive increase in rice production.

Fortunately, the ongoing applied research taking place on farms was doing very well. Despite the disastrous problems, shared equally across the islands with other farmers, yields in irrigated test lands achieved up to 5.8 tons per hectare, compared with the national average of 1.8 tons per hectare.

On rainfed land, the applied research farms produced equally good results, with yields of up to 4.1 ton per hectare, against the national average of only 1.2 tons. The research was being carried out under the name "Masagana 99." It was an important and prophetic name.

Masagana means "bountiful harvest" and *99* was the number of "cavans," or sacks, per hectare that was the yield target. A cavan weighs about a hundred pounds. To the average farmer, obtaining 99 cavans per hectare sounded like an impossible dream.

But the IRRI knew it needed dramatic results to persuade farmers. While the success of the scattered test sites was visible and convincing, it was not due entirely to the introduction of new plant strains. IRRI had introduced new credit programs, too, with loans in the form of fertilizer, seed, and other components of the total technical package. It also supplied ongoing advice from trained program technicians.

The early successful results, even in the face of natural disasters, had encouraged IRRI to begin training more extension specialists so it could enlarge its supervision of the on-farm demonstrations. Small villages—called "barrios"—were assigned to the new specialists. They were given motorcycles and went off into the countryside. Their job was to convince farmers that Masagana 99 was not an impossible dream.

As it turned out, the Masagana 99 program educated the bankers as clearly and as convincingly as it did the farmers. That year, rice was grown on 2,600 hectares with supervised credit, and on another 3,000 hectares using the IRRI practices, but with financing from other sources.

The barrios that had cooperative bankers were easy to spot. Where credit policies were liberal, 85 percent of the farmers were using the new technology. It was these farms that most impressed high officials in the government.

Many of the farmers using Masagana 99 technology topped 99 cavans per hectare, some harvesting as much as 145. Those who stuck to the old varieties and practices averaged only 40-65 cavans.

The government then decided to take the applied research technology tested by IRRI and extend it nationwide, under the same name—"Masagana 99." The result was phenomenal. In the year between July 1973 and June 1974 production of rice rose from 4.4 million to 5.5 million tons. This very nearly closed the gap between production and need in a single growing season. It took a lot of effort, but it was simple and direct in design.

The major instrument of change was supervised credit. Credit can be a creative use of the concept of money to catalyze potential into action. Under the Masagana 99 program, for instance, if a farmer wanted to finance his crop on credit he was not required to put up any collateral whatsoever. But he did have to do two things. One was to agree to follow the new techniques that the field technologists would teach him. The other was to join a *selda*, which is an informal group of between 5 and 15 farmers who are neighbors, friends, or relatives, and who agree to jointly and severally be responsible for one another's loans. To the banker, therefore, a *selda* is a joint liability group that signs a promisory note. To the farmer it is a moral obligation to the people closest to him.

The conversion to action was immediate. That year, more than 634,000 small scale farmers borrowed $87 million, compared to only 51,000 farmers with collateral who had borrowed $20 million the year before. The increase in credit was 329 percent, and the loans were spread over some 420 local rural banks, 102 branches of the Philippine National Bank, and 25 offices of the Government's Agricultural Credit Administration.

Each farmer was allowed credit up to $100 per hectare, enough to cover all his costs. Only part was given in cash—enough to cover the farmer's labor costs. The balance—for pesticides and fertilizer—was issued as purchase orders which were exchangeable for actual product at the local store. The storekeeper could redeem the purchase orders for cash at the bank. In many outlying areas, banks sent their own teams by Jeep, boat, or even helicopter to visit farmers, and process loans in the field.

The loans carried one percent per month interest, with maturity after six months. It was profitable business for the bankers who could discount promissory notes with the Central Bank, while 85 percent of the amounts loaned were guaranteed.

The approximately 634,000 farmers who availed themselves of the new credit opportunity represented an amazing 38 percent of all the rice farmers in the Philippines. However, they were not the only ones who joined Masagana 99; there were another 299,000 who did not require credit but only technical supervision. Together they totaled 933,000 Masagana 99 farmers, or an astounding 56 percent of all the rice farmers in the Philippines.

That figure becomes particularly outstanding when it is recalled that Masagana 99 was a completely voluntary program. It attracted many more farmers than originally expected. The total hectarage planted under Masagana 99 credit and technical supervision was 20 percent above the original targets. In rainfed land, it was 152 percent over target, which was particularly heartening because two-thirds of Philippine rice land depends on rainfall.

The best available field technologists were trained intensively in the new practices. During the wet season, there were 3,200 of these, each responsible for supervising 172 farmers. Even with motorcycles, this load was recognized as too heavy for a single individual. As soon as more technicians can be trained, the limiting problem will begin to diminish.

Despite their heavy work loads, the extension specialists on their motorcycles did very well. When they found a problem in a field, for instance, they often didn't take the time to locate the farmer to explain it to him personally. Instead, they simply stuck a tall bamboo pole with a yellow flag on it in that field; comments and instructions on how to correct the problem were taped to the shaft. The farmer saw the flag, read the instructions and corrected his problem. The farmers proved not to be difficult to deal with; indeed, they were eager for instruction that would improve their crops and, as a consequence, their incomes and their lives.

Where the Masagana farmer was concerned, the direct result was, simply, more cash in his pocket. The figures for the average farm of two to three hectares show that after paying all his costs—seed, labor, inputs, threshing, irrigation, bank loan, the lot—he doubled his net income from $276 to $575 per crop. And that is calculated at $6 per sack, which was the government's guaranteed support price. The actual market price was about $7.50 or 25 percent higher. The direct results of this were that he could start buying his land from his landlord under our nationwide land reform program, and he still had money to spend. Soon after the first harvest we noticed sharp increases in rural bus travel, children's enrollment in elementary and high schools, and consumer goods such as transistor radios, cooking stoves, soft drinks, and candies, to name only a few.

The indirect results of this were that the banker shed his hostility and found out that the small-scale farmer, and the new rice technology, could be a good credit risk even if there was no collateral. The farmer realized that government-sponsored loans were not political pork-barrel handouts and must be repaid. And the nation began to realize the credibility and sincerity of yet another program introduced by the government under the Philippine concept of martial law.

. . . from conference proceedings, 1974

Thus credit, in the form of crop loans without collateral, that also brought the new technology to the thousands of Philippine farmers (who till an average of 2.3 hectares each), was the single most important factor in the success of the program.

Another important aspect of the program—and a surprising one considering the frequently clumsy structures of government bureaus—was to teach the farmer the new technology for growing rice, and then make sure he followed it day-by-day, step-by-step. This required a government bureau to become an agency for the transfer of knowledge to the farmer from those who developed it, so the farmer could understand it and use it.

This difficult task was approached from three directions. The first involved the field technologists, whose job was to visit the farmer regularly and teach him the working procedures of the new technology—and to make sure he followed those procedures. The farmer needed demonstration and supervision in the correct use of fertilizer, the diagnosis of insect pest and plant disease problems, and instruction on their control. The field technologist had to teach the farmer what a *selda* was, and how to form one. He had to show the farmer how to get a bank loan, and advise him on the harvesting, threshing, storing, and marketing of his crop. Then he had to remind him to repay the bank loan. (The technologists succeeded here, too, as over 90 percent of the loans were repaid.) The field technologist was the personal link in the overall chain of direct participation.

The second approach to this problem of farmer education manifested as the biggest mass media communications campaign ever seen in the Philippines. The message was not carried, as might be expected, through TV and newspapers, because the farmers of Philippine villages do not own TV sets, and daily newspapers don't reach them. But three out of four farmers do have their own transistor radio and hold their local station in high esteem as a source of authority and knowledge.

So, in addition to a steady stream of spot announcements and musical jingles, 58 half-hour radio programs went out over the airwaves before dawn every day. In each province the local field technologist—the same man who supervised the farmer—conducted the radio program. He spoke the local dialect, knew the area, and was closely in touch with local crop conditions.

Besides the radio programs, hundreds of thousands of pocket-sized books were distributed, always in the local dialect or language. Each contained printed instructions in the new technology, divided into 16 easy-to-follow steps, plus everything else the farmer needed to know about Masagana 99.

This massive use of radio and booklets was supported by huge signboards outside the banks saying they lent money without collateral. Additional program support came from illustrated magazine articles, posters, membership flags for the Masagana farmers, vehicle stickers, and anything else that could provide further outreach to the potential audience in a given area.

In this way both appropriate mass communications media and field technologists were used to launch Masagana 99 as a nationwide program, much in the same way a major marketing organization might use the media and sales personnel to launch a new consumer product.

The third, and equally important system established to transfer this new knowledge to the farmers, and make sure they used it, was the creation of a tight governmental organization at every level.

The smallest political unit in the Philippines is the village, or barrio. There are a total of 34,000 barrios, each with its own elected officials. Each barrio was made responsible for forming its own *seldas*, for encouraging its farmers to join Masagana, and to grow more—and earn more—as a result.

In each of the 1,400 municipalities in the Philippines an action team was established, headed jointly by the mayor and the field technologist, along with the bank manager, and leaders of the surrounding barrios.

At the provincial level, the action committee was headed by the governor of the province and the provincial rice program officer, with representatives from the banks, the rice millers, traders, pesticide and fertilizer dealers, the local radio broadcasters, and all the local government agencies concerned with agriculture, local government, and land reform.

At the highest level, the overall Masagana 99 program was conducted by a national management committee comprised of leaders from both the government and private sectors.

Normally, a big government pyramid like this would be slowed down by its own red tape and bureaucratic procedures, so that however hard it pushed at the national level, only inertia and inefficiency would filter down to the barrios. Fortunately, this problem was recognized as a potential danger and prevented by several means. First, some of the top men in the Department of Agriculture were assigned to spend full time traveling around the country identifying problems, and solving them on the spot. The responsibility—and authority—to make decisions was decentralized and delegated downward to municipal and barrio levels. Each participant was told, further, that should anything go wrong that he and his immediate superiors could not solve, that situation was to be reported to Manila . . . and right away!

It was this total program commitment, supported by strong government action, that produced results. When President Marcos launched Masagana 99 as a nationwide program in May 1973, he said on nationwide radio and television, "If the national agencies, if those who participate in the private sector, the rural banks, the farmers . . . if you find anyone, whether in the public sector or the private sector, constituting an obstacle, an obstruction to the attainment of the objectives of Masagana 99, don't follow the ladder of leadership. If it is urgent, do something about it. If you cannot, and you think I must intervene, let me know, and I will intervene immediately . . . As of today, let everybody realize that Masagana 99 is a priority project!" With direct support from the President himself, everyone involved in the program—from the farmer to the government official—realized its importance.

Some of the results of the Masagana 99 program are startling and dramatic. Others, like the results of the World Food Production Conferences, are indirect and, though nearly impossible to measure, are equally real. These latter have to do not only with food and release from the immediate prospect of widespread hunger, but contributions to the general economic health and social stability of the world.

With the success of Masagana 99 the Philippines almost immediately approached self-sufficiency in rice. The need was 6.5 million tons, and the country harvested 5.5 million. The remainder was easily covered by carry-over stocks from the previous year, plus a small importation of rice that had already been contracted for. In larger, national terms, this resulted directly in the reduction of foreign exchange outflow.

For the smaller-scale concerns of the individual Masagana farmer, the direct result was simply more cash in his pocket. After paying all his costs—seed, labor, fertilizer, pesticides, threshing, irrigation, bank loan . . . the lot—the farmer doubled his net income from $276 to $575 per crop, based on the average farm of 2-3 hectares. That figure is calculated at $6 per cavan, which was the government's guaranteed support price, though the actual market price that year was about 25 percent higher. This meant the farmer could start buying land from his landlord under the Philippines nationwide land reform program and still have money left to spend. Soon after the first Masagana 99 harvest, sharp increases were observed in rural bus travel, enrollment in elementary and high schools, and in the sale of such consumer goods as transistor radios, cooking stoves, and soft drinks and candies, to name a few. All are considered indicators of real economic gains and genuine progress.

Some of the indirect results were equally important. Bankers shed their hostility when they discovered that the small scale farmer, with the new rice technology, could be a sound credit risk even without collateral. In his turn the farmer realized that government-sponsored loans were not political pork-barrel handouts, and required repayment.

At the end of the first year's program President Marcos appeared again on the public airwaves to review the results, saying, ". . . Truly, the Masagana 99 program was a triumph of cooperation between many sectors of our society, working hand-in-hand, in unison and in concert. It was a triumph of unity. What this means is that the basic machinery for the attainment of self-sufficiency in rice production has been established, tested, and proven sound. It only remains for us to correct what little deficiencies remain, to plug the small loopholes, to add the little touches. The fundamental structure, however, has been built."

Success, of course, is only the foundation for more success. Thus, in the Philippines the struggle for increased rice production has only begun. A program to study typhoons has been undertaken in the hope that ways can be found to divert them, or lessen their impact on crops. A crop-insurance program is also being established to protect the farmer from economic loss from weather or pestilence.

Demand for fertilizer has, naturally, increased in the Philippines. During the first big Masagana 99 year of 1973-74, 381,000 tons were allocated to food crops—principally rice. This was 92 percent more than the previous year. For 1974-75, a commitment was made to increase the supply an additional 38 percent.

Looking toward further rural improvement, the loan ceiling per farmer has been raised to cover the increased cost of required inputs. The Philippine National Bank is buying additional vehicles to act as mobile banks that will go out to the farmers and process loans right in the barrios. Within five years, the number of rural banks will be doubled, and more field technologists are continuously being trained in the latest agricultural practices for rice.

By the next crop year a 20 percent increase in the number of farmers enrolled in the Masagana 99 program is expected.

To ease the strain of getting the rice to market, more feeder roads are being built from the farms. And the price support program will be maintained so the farmer is secure in the market, even if the price of rice falls below the guarantee.

New irrigation systems are being constructed and older

systems repaired. At present only 35 percent of the land in rice has controlled irrigation. For that reason, large scale experimentation is taking place in 50,000 rainfed hectares with what is called Direct Seeding. It's an interesting new development.

Normally, on rainfed farms, the farmer sows rice seed into a seedbed and lets it grow there for about 25 days. During this time he is preparing his fields by plowing, harrowing, and applying fertilizer. Ideally, the growing seedlings should be transplanted from the seedbed to the field when they are 25 days old, but this assumes that enough rain has fallen in the fields. Two potential problems are created for the farmer in this procedure. The first is that he never knows exactly when the rains will start. If the rains are two weeks late, for example, his seedlings will be about 40 days old at the time of transplant, sharply reducing their yield.

The second potential problem is at the other end. Normally, the rice farmer plants during June, transplants in July when the rains are heaviest, and harvests around October. From September to October, the crops need plenty of rain plus a few dry sunny days. But usually September and October are sunny months with only a little rain. So the problem is the risk of drought during the last 30 days of the crop, which will also reduce the yield.

The Direct Seeding process offers better odds for resolving those two problems. First, it eliminates the seedbed. As soon as the first light rains come in May, and the soil is moist, the seed is sown directly into the field. That puts it at least one month ahead of the rice that is transplanted in the conventional way. The seed used is a newly-developed variety which matures in 95 days, as against the other new high-yielding varieties which require up to 120 days from sowing. That factor gains another month.

Therefore, by sowing in May, and harvesting in August—and from July to August there is normally plenty of rainfall—the farmer avoids the drier period from September to October. Also, August and September are traditionally months when there is no harvesting in the Philippines, which means market supplies are short and prices are high. Now, after an August harvest, if his land is low-lying and can hold water from the lighter rains to come, the farmer can plant a second crop of rice. Or, if he farms in an upland area, he can plant a crop of vegetables.

This experimentation, already proving successful, is aimed at a potential of 900,000 farmers on rainfed lands, almost half the total area planted to rice.

The indicators of continued and improved success are so high that crops other than rice are benefitting from the new technology. At the present time the basic system employed by the Masagana 99 program is being used to increase the production of corn, soybeans, and sorghum. The same credit is allowed without collateral. The same technical supervision is supplied, and the same massive transfer of knowledge to the farmer is taking place.

The foundation for real, genuine prosperity among the two-thirds of the Philippine population that tills the soil and feeds the nation has been established. Masagana 99 is a success story almost without parallel in the struggle for massive increases in food production, and much needed improvement in the overall standards of living in developing countries.

Most assuredly, it stands as an example of what can be done with cooperation, with the interest and concern of all disciplines related to agriculture, and with the strong support of a government determined to develop agricultural productivity.

In presenting this story of Philippine success—the Masagana 99 story—to the conferees at the Tenth Asia/Pacific Food Production Conference in Tokyo, the Secretary of Agriculture and National Resources of the Republic of the Philippines closed his address with the following:

> ". . . One final word . . . the application of this program to other countries is, of course, clear. I will not insult you by specifying how these applications can be made. Certainly, where farmers are in the bonds of usury and are unable to obtain credit, there must be credit for them if they are to be able to produce, and produce well. Certainly farmers need technology. All of you know that farmers welcome technology, contrary to those writers who sit behind their desks and say that farmers are resistant to change. I have not found a farmer yet who is resistant to change . . . he welcomes change and, given the protection and minimization of risk, he always accepts change. Therefore, where he needs technology, the skillful use of field technicians and mass media is certainly a critical element in the program.
>
> "Finally, in the world of Watergate and wars, it seems to me that we have shown what a country can do for the least of its peo-

ple, when united under a strong government. In a world of inflation and economic chaos, it seems to me that there are invaluable lessons here for us, and for the rest of the world.

"I noticed in the IMC presentation earlier . . . the first part of this program . . . there was a very poignant phrase saying 'when agriculture fails, there are no dreams.' I would like to paraphrase one of the favorite sayings of the late and great statesman of the United States, Robert Kennedy. He said, 'Others see things as they are and ask, why? We dream things that never were and ask, why not?' We have asked ourselves in the Philippines, why not? And we have proven that we can achieve dreams that never were . . . Thank you."

. . .from conference proceedings, 1974

after the green revolution

Much has been experienced, and much has been learned since the first World Food Production Conference in 1965. Now, ten years later, it seems as important in retrospect as it seemed to those engaged in its development at the time. For today the subject of increased food production is a credible subject worldwide. While then, it seemed, no one was taking the time to put the subject in perspective, so that something could be done to improve it.

A great deal has been accomplished in the last decade. Not that there yet is sufficient food for all the peoples of the earth. Nor that hunger is less of a reality to those millions of unfortunates who suffer it as companion of their days—and as bed partner every night of their lives.

No, the end of the problem is not yet in sight. But, at last, major attention is being paid to the subject. The United Nations held a World Food Conference in Rome in 1974, and a great deal of coverage was given by the press and the media to this worldwide expression of concern. That conference is beginning to produce results, as the huge wheels of international government are finally being made to turn.

U.S. Secretary of State Henry Kissinger was quoted in *Time* as having asked, rhetorically, "Who would have thought of an international food policy, or a World Food Conference, ten years ago. Today it is only a question of time until we develop it. The real question is: Will we develop it soon enough? I think we can."

The story of the World Food Production Conferences unfolded in this book is one answer to Dr. Kissinger's question about who would have thought of it. In fact, materials and information gained from the IMC conferences were used to assist U.S. government officials in their preparation for the United Nations World Food Conference in Rome, a contribution acknowledged by IMC being selected as one of few American businesses invited to send "private sector" observers to the UN session.

The company was, of course, glad to be of service in an effort of this scale that would help focus the spotlight of awareness on worldwide hunger, and the pressing need for ever-increasing food availability.

For that need is, in many ways, as great now as it was a decade ago. There have been many advances, to be sure, but there has also been bad weather and other circumstances that slowed up the advances. The future remains uncertain. World population, increasing at the average annual rate of 2 percent, grew by 700 million people—from 3.2 billion in 1964, to 3.9 billion in 1974. If the same rate of growth is maintained for another decade, world population will add another 855 million people, more than the entire population of India today. These projections suggest the haunting laugh of Malthus coming back again to quench the spirit of the times.

But Dr. Kissinger's comment on his own question indicates that present world awareness of food shortfall will lead toward the establishment of machinery to overcome it. It is only a question of time, he says, and then states his belief that it can be accomplished in time to head off major disaster.

That same belief in possibility has been the underlying spirit of the World Food Production Conferences from their beginnings. It continues still. At the Lima, Peru conference in 1974, the president of IMC, R. A. Lenon, was among the panelists. In his opening remarks, he summed up world concerns, and reintroduced IMC's corporate faith in the conferences.

> "... As you well know, we meet this year in an atmosphere of growing concern about food supply. This year we are not the only ones gathering to seek solutions to world food production problems. We welcome increased attention to the problem, and we feel that this added emphasis offers new hope for the future.
>
> "You who are gathered here share in the distinguished tradition of the oldest continuing series of meetings dedicated to seeking solutions to the problems of world hunger and malnutrition through increased food production.
>
> "When IMC sponsored the first Latin American Food Production Conference, in Caracas in 1965, its purposes were to provide a forum for the advancement of ideas that would help individual nations achieve food efficiency, and to promote international concern for a growing food problem.
>
> "These are still our objectives. Our motivations are the same.
>
> "As the world's largest independent producer of fertilizer raw materials, we have leadership responsibility in an area of great

concern to all citizens. We recognize that further solutions are the responsibility of both the private and public sector, and IMC has long sought to facilitate the cooperation between men of industry, science and government.

"These conferences are not the only way in which our company has attempted to cooperate internationally. For almost twenty-five years, we have conducted a variety of industry-oriented training programs in management and fertilizer technology. Students and trainees from all over the world have participated in our training programs. We shall continue this work, just as we plan to continue our support of these World Food Production Conferences.

"Over the past two years there have been dramatic declines in food reserves, making it imperative that we accelerate programs for more food production in both the developed and developing countries. Because of this—and further aggravating the situation—we have also experienced a temporary shortage of fertilizer materials.

"IMC has committed itself to helping solve this new problem. Last year alone, we invested more than $80 million in new plants and expanded production. This current year, we have already committed more than $100 million to further expand manufacturing and mining facilities. Projects involving an additional $150 million are being considered. These figures indicate the breadth of our commitment—and we are only one company!

"Many of our plans and activities involve programs of an international nature—through new partnerships and joint ventures—so that fertilizer supplies can be made available in those areas where they are most needed. Other fertilizer companies, public and private, are mounting equally aggressive responses to the shortage problem. In total, given the building program now underway and planned, most fertilizer materials will be available in reasonable quantities by 1976 or 1977. After that, more building has to be planned, and the planning has to begin now.

"Obviously, it is not enough to merely make fertilizer available. The technology of fertilizer usage in connection with the new high yielding varieties, and meeting local soil and water conditions, is now of greater importance than ever before. This will require intensified crop and fertilizer research geared to local conditions in various parts of the world.

"In recognition of this need, IMC has chosen to take 'the initiative in providing funds for local fertilizer research effort here in Peru, through the auspices of the International Potato Research Center at La Molina. This grant will hopefully support new activity

*with regard to fertilizer usage, and will serve to complement the
ongoing activities of this internationally recognized center . . ."*

. . . from conference proceedings, 1974

At the Asia/Pacific Food Production Conference that same
year, IMC announced a similar grant to the Asian Vegetable
Research and Development Center at Shanhua, Taiwan, under
the direction of conferee Dr. Robert F. Chandler.

This decade of conferences has seen a great many changes on
the face of world agriculture. Ten years is a considerable span of
time, and if you are among the hungry awaiting a resolution to
the problem, helpless to affect it yourself, it is an even longer
time. It is unfortunate for those at the end of the line, but time
is the principal factor in progress.

Ten years ago the International Rice Research Institute and
the International Center for the Improvement of Maize and
Wheat were virtually the only international research programs
affecting food production. Since that time an international network of ten research programs has been established. It is supported by 29 governments, foundations, and organizations,
under the chairmanship of the World Bank. Research is being
conducted on vegetables, beans, beef, potatoes and other root
and tuber crops, chick peas, groundnuts, animal diseases, the
concerns of African herdsmen, and a good many other things.
Each of these will—when successful—be able to help farmers
function productively on the land of even the remote, small-
scale farms of the developing nations. Research is the foundation of the belief in the capability of man to continue to grow
food for the world family.

But research by itself will not be able to get the results required for the future. Much, if not most, of those results will
be based on the transmission to the farmer of knowledge about
soil fertility and farming methods, and how to work with the
new plant strains; much will depend on the amount of irrigation
that can be brought to the land; and much will depend on the
infrastructure of each nation so that the product of the farm
can be brought to market and put into the hands of those who
need it including, especially, those who need it most.

The world already possesses the ability; what it now needs
is to develop the capability. It takes 80 percent of a nation's

people, in some cases, to grow less than enough food for their needs, while a farmer in the U.S.S.R. can feed six additional people, and an American farmer is capable of feeding 46! We know how to do that. While the Asian farmer spends five days in the fields to grow 100 lbs. of grain, an American farmer might only spend five minutes. That is capability. It can be developed and spread.

Research is important, especially important, to tomorrow. Today is the time when the benefits of yesterday's research needs to be at work in the fields of the world, growing food for record harvests. To be able to accomplish that dissemination of farming capability would ease the problem almost by itself. It is, as a practical matter, the only means of continuing immediate improvement.

A large part of the spreading of technology depends on such mundane concerns as the prompt and timely arrival of needed inputs, such as fertilizer, when it is necessary that it be incorporated into the fields. When, in days gone by, fertilizer was in ample supply, this posed little problem. But as more and more fertilizer was put into the service of increasing food production, and when the price of oil—from which some fertilizer is made—quadrupled suddenly, the available stocks of fertilizer fell, and the product came into short supply.

Fertilizer is not, of course, the only agricultural input so affected, but the problems associated with it are typical of a new enigma being faced by farmers everywhere, and particularly those of the developing nations.

Much as the after-harvest loss of grain to rodents and insects was taking a substantial percentage of all grain harvested, the pre-planting loss of fertilizer to the farmers was taking another big bite out of their productive yields. It wasn't, perhaps, as direct or dramatic a loss but, in a fertilizer-short period, there was much concern. It was vital that fertilizer be obtained and stored so as to be accessible when needed. Changes in the market had forced the question, "What do you do when the demand for the product has outstripped production of the product? How can you best deal with that circumstance?" In one way or another, that question was on the minds of many conferees.

It was the kind of question—one having a direct bearing on food production—that the conference was designed to deal with. And at the tenth anniversary of the founding of the conferences, it was appropriate that this subject be explored by

Neal Schenet, an IMC Vice President, and the executive who—
with Anthony Cascino, the conference's founding chairman—
developed the original thinking that had led to the conferences.
Mr. Schenet encapsulated the story of previous meetings in
the Asia/Pacific, and the kind of practical approach that had
been taken to problems of increasing food production. He said
of the latter that "it has changed the face of Asia."

Calling attention to the warehousing problems that had
dominated the previous year's conference, with particular emphasis on the problem of protecting food supplies once they
have been produced, he indicated that the problem of warehousing fertilizer in times of short supply was a credit to the
success of previous conferences, and to the success of fertilizer
in making more food than before grow wherever it was used.
Then he addressed the present situation directly and practically:

> "In any shortage period, the first step any consumer must take is to
> accommodate himself to the realities of the market supply situation.
> He must be ready to take product when it's available, and in the
> quantities offered! This may sound like a one-way street, a produ-
> cer's story; unfortunately, it's the only way to survive.
>
> "Fine, you may say, but how do I take a product without storage
> space? One possible answer that I want you to seriously consider
> today is "Outdoor Storage."
>
> "Let me be clear at the outset—this practice is neither untried nor
> untested. We have mentioned it in several presentations, and some
> of you may have discussed it with our people at home. We want to
> bring you today a wrap-up on outdoor storage.
>
> "In the past, we may have been a little hesitant about recom-
> mending the use of outdoor storage for three very good reasons.
> One, we weren't in the middle of a product shortage. Two, indoor
> storage was available and, therefore, extra storage wasn't such a
> critical problem. And three, it wasn't a proven practice, and we were
> still testing the practice ourselves. Today, I think we can safely re-
> fute all of these arguments."

. . . from conference proceedings, 1974

He then began that process of transferring knowledge that had
suddenly become important. The loss of fertilizer to the growth

of food was as important as the traditional "loss of a nail" which led to the loss of a kingdom. And, the reason for its having been introduced at the conference, was related by Mr. Schenet:

> *"I might make one supplemental comment. Last summer we were pleased to have a group of overseas visitors with us for several weeks as a part of our fertilizer management training program. One of the topics that seemed to be bothering them most was the problem of outdoor storage and the ability to take products whenever they were available, since they weren't always able to get product when their bins were empty. So, they said, they would appreciate it very much if we would put something together on this subject. Even though many people have tried outdoor storage, there are those who have not, and so don't know all of the pros and cons. That's the reason we included it in the program, and why we are developing a new manual on this which will soon be coming to you. It will include many more of the technical details, so your technicians can actually work from it."*

> *. . . from conference proceedings, 1974*

One presentation at the Tenth World Food Production Conference summed up the decade of progress, and focused attention and thoughts on the challenge that lay immediately ahead. The questions seemed to be framing the future for the conferees:

> *"The human species has but one home in which to live. How we manage the resources of that earthly home in the coming decade may well determine if mankind is ultimately to become an endangered species . . .*
>
> *"Ahead is a decade of critical challenge. We move into the future, a future dark and unclear. Only if we search the darkness by the light of penetrating questions, will we be able to fashion the solutions of survival. . . .*
>
> *"We look ahead to 1984. Do we see a world whose people are dependent on an international 'Big Brother,' or a world of self-reliance and international cooperation?*
>
> *"It is for us, assembled here, to ask the hardest question: Will*

the growth of population outstrip the growth of food; will chronic malnutrition and hunger then give way to outright starvation?

"Without waiting for an answer, we must ask 'What can we do to increase world food production?' Within that question lie all other questions . . .

"To most people in the world, fertilizer is the difference between food and no food. Each million tons of reduction in fertilizer nutrients represents a loss of 10 million tons in grain. Where will the supply come from?

"Will we somehow coordinate the efforts of people who are exploring the world for raw materials? The challenge is to mine more phosphate and potash, to build more nitrogen plants.

"But you can have the fertilizer you need, be willing to export it, and not have the transportation to deliver. Will we convince the shipbuilders to build more ships, the railroads to build more cars?

"Are there dramatic developments on the horizon of fertilizer technology? Might we someday put the raw material right in the ground, pour some acid on it, cover it up and plant the seed, and so create a fertilizer factory in the soil?

"Or can we have an ocean-going factory? Can we load a ship in the U.S. with phosphate rock, potash, and solid nitrogen, manu-facture en route, *and unload it in Thailand as finished fertilizer? . . .*

"We must produce what we need. We will, if we act with courage and decision on a broad spectrum of problems, despite all the difficulties. We must look ahead, not to a time of threat, but to a Decade of Challenge.

"Man has become what he is because he alone can ask questions about that which troubles him and seek for solutions.

"The questions we ask now, and the answers to follow, will in great measure determine the questions we ask ten years from now. We start to ask them here. Now."

. . . from conference proceedings, 1974

With all of the thought and planning, the reshaping of the cor-porate molecule, and the prodigious efforts of those individu-als—both sponsors and conferees—the result was that after ten years considerable progress had been made in the struggle to produce increasing amounts of food for the earth's increasing number of people.

The progress had not been a rocket's rise into the skies of

plenty, but neither had it been so anticipated. After ten years of dedicated conference effort, the world's problem was still hunger, and food was still the world's greatest need.

In ten years the problem had not been solved. The possibility that it may never be was recognized. There had been rises of hope, and falls of failure. But the commitment of the world's farmers to their land was a continuing inspiration to the commitment of the conferees, each of whom—by his presence and contributing interest—shared in the successes, and was wounded by the failures.

But the commitment continues. And that is, perhaps, the most remarkable chapter in the still-unfolding story of the World Food Production Conferences. It is the still unwritten chapter of the future. For, after a decade of maintaining its focus on increased food production, the conference sees ahead much of the same challenge. Agriculture has come a long way from the early promise of von Liebig's discoveries, and it fortunately still remains some distance from the dark prognosis of Malthus. The question has not been answered and perhaps it will never be answered. But the indications are clear that food is lord of human life, and that by increasing its production it is possible to at least quiet the storm of hunger. Some day not too distant, man may be able to produce food faster than he reproduces himself. It is a sound thought, for efforts to increase food production are being joined by efforts to curtail the growth of population. The answer to how successful these efforts will be is still some years—even decades—away.

But, meanwhile, there is still room for hope and for commitment to that hope. That continues to be the basis of the World Food Production Conferences, and that continues to be the philosophy of its sponsor, IMC. The new corporate molecule has taken a firm hold on its hope for increasing food production to feed the world. It still bends its corporate efforts in that direction.

Ten years is a long time for privately-sponsored annual conferences to last, particularly those of an international nature. Yet the World Food Production Conferences, in 1975, begin their second decade of service. No longer are their voices lonely, or shielded by unconcern from exposure to the world. They have become vibrant and important fixtures among the other elements attacking the world's greatest problem.

Its hundreds of conferees and other participants have been

in the vanguard force of volunteers battling the enemy—human hunger. In their struggle, they have come to know with a certainty that man is, indeed, capable and that the only instrumentality that can keep agriculture from its potential capability is man himself. If man *will*, he *can*; but if man neglects this potential, hunger will persist. Not man-made, perhaps, but man-maintained. It could be said by the conference, as the late Walt Kelly so eloquently expressed it in the comic strip *Pogo*, "We have met the enemy, and he is us!"

The history of these conferences is a tribute to those who participated in the exchange of how-to-do-it information, and who kept their concerns vitally entwined with a determination of the true contemporary relationship between food, population and hunger. The conferences have been the joint success of those many conferees, a good number of whom remained steadfast throughout many years of meetings.

The role of the conferences in the future is expected to be much like it has been in the past: strong, hopeful and practical, seeing to it that vital information is passed along and made useful, within its own sphere of expertise.

It is a proud history to carry into the future. In his closing address to a decade, Conference Chairman Sidney Keel summed it up . . . past, present and future:

> *"I promise you this is the final talk of this year's World Food Production Conference. And it is a pleasure I have reserved to myself!*
>
> *"One of the greatest pleasures, of course, has been witnessing the wholehearted participation and contributions of each of you in this year's conference.*
>
> *"The two major objectives of these conferences have always been to provide a forum where ideas could be freely exchanged, and to call the world's attention to the problems of global hunger and malnutrition. In this, they have been successful. The problems have been clearly defined. And they have been addressed strongly and positively.*
>
> *"This is the tenth year we have gathered to consider the latest statistics on world hunger. There are, as we've discussed, major differences in the atmosphere of this year's meeting.*
>
> *"One well-publicized difference is that we are no longer the only ones meeting to attack the problems of hunger and search for practical solutions.*

"No sooner was a World Food Conference proposed to the U.N. General Assembly just a year ago, than a host of organizations— colleges, banks, agricultural associations, and trade groups—convened world food conferences of their own, in such widely scattered locations as London, Chicago, Des Moines, and Washington, D.C. Today we hear a rising chorus of voices, each straining to be heard, each with its own predictions and its own recommendations.

"And we are glad. *We welcome their contribution.*

"Because only with worldwide concern and international cooperation can the steps be taken to find medium term solutions to the problem of hunger—and a long term approach *to both the problems of population growth and toward the ultimate goal of food sufficiency for all.*

"We've heard that we've been pretty lucky over the past ten years. That somehow we've managed to muddle through without a major outbreak of famine. I'm not so sure this information would be very comforting to the hundreds of thousands—maybe as many as a million—who have perished from starvation in the Sahel region of Africa during the past two years.

"Traditionally, when the world was faced with the threat of widespread famine, the U.S. grain reserve was the insurance. And even though that reserve is just about gone today, being down to about a 26-day supply, everyone is keeping his fingers crossed hoping that those reserves will somehow be replenished.

"The U.S. had, in fact, hoped for a bumper crop this year. But, because of weather, it isn't going to happen. Instead, the major share of an anticipated 35 million ton shortfall in the world's grain harvest will probably be borne by the U.S.

"But statistics being quoted at other conferences would seem to give rise to an expectation that the U.S. can still protect the world against widespread famine.

"This seems to be what a lot of people are hoping for—and even expecting.

"Well, I think it is time we really faced facts.

"Obviously we are not *going to return to the "status quo" of a few years ago. The United States can no longer provide all the resources for the world. Even with a continued increase in U.S. food production, there will be no new U.S. grain reserve to insure the needs of the rest of the world.*

"This means that importing countries will now have to assume more of the responsibility for maintaining their own reserves, or be prepared to compete for supplies in the marketplace. Rather than

waiting for the need to manifest itself in outbreaks of famine, they will have to concentrate on gearing up to grow the bulk of their own food requirements.

"Let's put the problems into perspective. What is the state of food production in the developing countries?

"It differs, of course, from country to country. In 32 out of 72 developing countries for which data is available, food output grew faster than demand between 1966 and 1972.

"Even in 1972—which has since proven to be the crisis year—food production in the developing countries was 20 percent higher than in 1966, the latest previous year of bad weather.

"These considerable achievements reflect dramatic and effective application of technology in many countries. However, it was not vigorous or effective enough.

"It does, though, emphasize that progress has been made, and that the potential *for increasing food production does exist.*

"The most immediate potential is, of course, to increase production on that land that is now under *cultivation. And here there is room for tremendous improvement.*

"While many countries have achieved tremendous progress in employing new technology, many others have done little or nothing in overcoming traditional and nonproductive practices. In many cases this is not because of a lack of resources, or international cooperation, but because of a particular country's own policies, and the apparent lack of urgency it gives to increasing its own local food production.

"But, the objective of our meeting is not to point our fingers at nations which have faltered in their development efforts. Rather, our goal is to seek solutions and get the job done.

"It is, of course, impossible to consider the problems in achieving food self-sufficiency without recognizing the extreme pressure of the population explosion. A world which has succeeded in saving and prolonging life has an equal responsibility in providing for the health and fulfillment of those lives. One cannot accept one responsibility without the other. There is new hope in a growing realization of this fact. Perhaps the real hope lies in the growing experience of many countries that the economic improvement of people is followed by a decline in birth rate, and a trend toward a controlled population.

"Let me close these remarks with one final example. I would like to speak in this instance, not as your conference chairman but, as an officer of IMC. I've touched very briefly during my remarks

on the need for more efficient utilization of fertilizers. We at IMC have accepted this challenge—and are doing something tangible about it in at least four directions (and I might say that all of these activities can be, and in some cases, are being carried out by the entire fertilizer industry—not just my company).

(1) Provision of technical assistance overseas.

Here we are providing qualified production technicians to assist developing countries in raising the level of production in fertilizer plants. It has been documented that the average rate of productive capacity of fertilizer plants in the developing countries is no higher than 60 percent. While some of this is due to factors over which we have no control, such as power stoppages, and so on, some of the loss can certainly be prevented by application of skilled productive know-how.

(2) Massive agricultural research grants in developing countries.

Some of the problems of food production stem from improper agronomic practices, lack of information on effects of various fertilizers on crops indigenous to the developing countries, and detail on how to make more efficient use of restricted fertilizer supplies. In an effort to overcome these problems to a major degree, we are making research grants on a regular basis to such groups as those studying rice in the Philippines, potatoes in Latin America, vegetables in South East Asia, and others. Our program visualizes a growth in this program to as much as a quarter of a million dollars per year.

(3) The continued sponsorship of the World Food Production Conference.

We believe this is a vital forum for international exchange of ideas and information related to the growth of more food, where, as you know, no question amenable to practical resolution is too large or too small. At a past conference two hours were once spent on determining what kind of burlap should be used for fertilizer bags. It was an issue of some local consequence, because in the economy of that part of the world burlap has important reuse applications that range from clothing to bedcovers. The after-use value of the bag made fertilizer more attractive to local farmers, and this stimulus to fertilizer use helped increase food production.

(4) IMC Customer Training Programs.

We believe in increasing the efficient use of fertilizer for greater food production. Efficiency can be developed, so every year we host customer trainees from around the world in fertilizer technol-

ogy and management—over 6,000 to date. These fertilizer industry people come to IMC-sponsored seminars, clinics, symposia, and workshops. Training is tailored to the needs of the particular individual, or group. It is conducted by IMC people representing skills in administration and finance, production and distribution, agronomy and research, marketing and sales, insurance and purchasing. Today, 32 nations have better qualified fertilizer producers—and greater food production—because IMC customers go back to school!

"These are just a few of the things we, as one company, and the total industry can do and are doing. If more action programs such as these are undertaken, less talk programs will be needed.

"Years ago, Wendell Wilkie spoke of 'One World'—in many respects, far ahead of his time. Today, facing the spectre of world hunger and the related fertilizer crisis, we have come full circle, and finally must realize that we can no longer be nationalists but are truly citizens of the world.

"The will—that is the crux of the challenges that confront us this year.

"We must have the will to act.

"The necessity to act has been thrust upon us all.

"It is now up to us—as individuals, as companies, as developing and developed countries, as United Nations, as citizens of the world—to do so."

. . . from conference proceedings, 1974

Hunger can't wait. Let the work begin!

appendixes

WORLD FOOD PRODUCTION CONFERENCES:
DATES AND LOCATIONS

1965   SKOKIE, ILLINOIS, March
        HONG KONG, April
        CARACAS, VENEZUELA, May
        PARIS, FRANCE, June

1966   TOKYO, JAPAN, February
        SAN JUAN, PUERTO RICO, March

1967   SYDNEY, AUSTRALIA, February
        MEXICO CITY, MEXICO, April

1968   BANGKOK, THAILAND, March
        BUENOS AIRES, ARGENTINA, April

1969   SINGAPORE, March
        RIO DE JANEIRO, BRAZIL, April

1970   MANILA, PHILIPPINES, March
        SANTIAGO, CHILE, April

1971   NEW DELHI, INDIA, January
        MEDELLIN, COLOMBIA, March

1972   SEOUL, KOREA, September
        SAO PAULO, BRAZIL, November

1973   JAKARTA, INDONESIA, September
        SAN SALVADOR, EL SALVADOR, November

1974   LIMA , PERU, September
        TOKYO, JAPAN, October

1975   KUALA LUMPUR, MALAYSIA, October
        SANTO DOMINGO, DOMINICAN REPUBLIC, November

CONFERENCE PARTICIPANTS

Mr. S. K. Agrawal, Division Manager
The Minerals & Metals Trading Corporation of India
New Delhi, India

Mr. Nuruddin Ahmed
Shaikh Deen & Khans, Ltd.
Dacca, Bangladesh

Dr. Rodolfo Antonelli, Director
Industria Agro Pecuaria, S.A.
Sao Paulo, Brazil

Sr. Alfonso Ardizzoni, President
Cia. Sud America de Fosfatos, S.A.
Santiago, Chile

Mr. W. Asai, General Manager
Fertilizer & Pesticide Department
Zen-Noh, Tokyo, Japan

A. W. Aspen, Sales Manager
IMC (New York)
New York, New York, U.S.A.

Sr. Roberto Astralaga, Gerente General
Abonos Colombianos, S.A.
Bogota, Colombia

Mr. Harvey Auman, Vice President
Canpotex Limited
Toronto, Ontario, Canada

Mr. Jacinto Avalos, President
Fertilizantes Fosfatados Mexicanos, S.A.
Mexico, D.F., Mexico

Ing. Julio Eduardo Aznarez, Presidente
Comision Honoraria del Plan Agropecuario
Montevideo, Uruguay

Dr. Antonia Bacigalupo, Director Investigacion
Universidad Nacional Agraria
La Molina, Lima, Peru

Mr. Alden Berry, General Manager
ICI (ANZ)
Melbourne, Australia

Mr. David Berry, General Manager
Western Mining Corporation Limited
Melbourne, Australia

Mr. M. R. Bhide, Executive Chairman
Voltas Limited
Bombay, India

Sr. Luis Bocalatto, President
Cia Paulista de Adubos
Sao Paulo, Brazil

Dr. Norman E. Borlaug, Nobel Laureate and Director
International Maize & Wheat Improvement Center
Mexico, D. F., Mexico

Mr. Marc Boudier, Administrative Director
S.I.P.E.C.E.O.
Saigon, Vietnam

Dr. Reid A. Bryson, Director
Institute for Environmental Studies
University of Wisconsin
Madison, Wisconsin, U.S.A.

Mr. S. M. H. Burney, Joint Secretary to Government of India
Ministry of Food and Agriculture
New Delhi, India

Mr. Alan W. Bryant, Director Superintendent
Cia Petroquimica Brasileria (COPEBRAS)
Sao Paulo, Brazil

Sr. Ary Burger, Agricultural Credit Director
Banco Central de Brazil
Rio de Janeiro, Brazil

Sr. Alberto Caprile, President
Ganados, S.A.
Buenos Aires, Argentina

Sr. Fernando P. Cardoso, President
Manah, S.A.
Sao Paulo, Brazil

Mr. A. E. Cascino, Executive Vice President
International Minerals & Chemical Corporation
Libertyville, Illinois, U.S.A.

Sr. Jose Castillo, Presidente
Agricultural Development Bank
San Salvador, El Salvador

Dr. Robert C. Chandler, Jr., Director
International Rice Research Institute
Los Banos, Philippines

Mr. W. W. Chadwick, President
Phosphate Rock Export Association
Tampa, Florida, U.S.A.

Mr. K. Y. Chow, Managing Director
Thai Oil Refinery Co.
Bangkok, Thailand

Dr. S. D. Chowdhury, Consultant Agricultural Division
Planning Commission
Government of Bangladesh
Dacca, Bangladesh

H. E. Luis Fernando Cirne Lima, Minister of Agriculture
Republic of Brazil
Brasilia, Brazil

Dr. Norman Collins, Program Advisor in Agriculture
The Ford Foundation
Santiago, Chile

Mr. Gerald T. Coughlin, Manager
Quinonez Hermanos, S.A.
San Salvador, El Salvador

Dr. Milo Cox, Associate Director Agriculture
Technical Assistance Bureau, USAID
Washington, D.C., U.S.A.

Mr. K. B. K. Currie, General Manager
Guthrie Waugh & Co.
Kuala Lumpur, Malaysia

Ing. Mario D'Agosto, Director Gerente
Industria Sulfurica, S.A.
Montevideo, Uruguay

Mr. Bharat C. Dalal, General Manager
Gujarat State Fertilizer Company, Ltd.
Baroda, India

Mr. S. L. Dev, Sales Manager
Agriculture Chemicals
Voltas Limited
New Delhi, India

Mr. Johnson Douglas, Associate Director
The Rockefeller Foundation
New Delhi, India

Mr. Judson H. Drewry, Vice President
International Minerals & Chemical Corporation
Libertyville, Illinois, U.S.A.

Mr. Erik Ekedahl, Sales Manager Asia/Pacific
International Minerals & Chemical Corporation
Libertyville, Illinois, U.S.A.

Sr. Hernan Elgueta, Vice President
Sociedad Quimica Y Minera, S.A.
Santiago, Chile

Dr. Raymond Ewell, Professor of Chemical Engineering
State University of New York
Buffalo, New York, U.S.A.

Mr. Paul Faberson, Division Vice President
International Minerals & Chemical Corporation
Libertyville, Illinois, U.S.A.

Sr. Paulo Figueiredo, Superintendent Director
Agrofertil, S.A.
Sao Paulo, Brazil

Dr. John W. Fitts, Director
International Soil Fertility Evaluation & Improvement Program, USAID
North Carolina State University
Raleigh, North Carolina, U.S.A.

Mr. Chujiro Fujino, President
Mitsubishi Corporation
Tokyo, Japan

Sr. Clovis Galante, President
IAP, S.A., Industria Agro-Pecuaria
Sao Paulo, Brazil

Ing. Augusto Gamio Palacio, Gerente General
Fertiperu
Lima, Peru

Dr. Eusbio F. Garcia, President
Chemical Industries of the Philippines
Manila, Philippines

Sr. Marcelino Garcia, Sales Manager
Phosphate Rock Export Association
Tampa, Florida, U.S.A.

Mr. E. Thurman Gaskill, Farmer
Corwith, Iowa, U.S.A.

Mr. A. E. Gaze, General Manager
British Phosphate Commission
Melbourne, Australia

Dr. Jose Drummond Goncalves, Presidente
Associacao Nacional para Difusao de Adubos (ANDA)
Sao Paulo, Brazil

Mr. Leonides P. Gonzalez, Executive Vice President
Planter's Products, Inc.
Manila, Philippines

Mr. Alexander Grobman, Director
Investigacion y Desarrollo para America Latina
Northrup, King & Co.
Lima, Peru

Sr. Rodolfo Gurdian, President
Abonos Superior, S.A.
San Jose, Costa Rica

Dr. Ki Hak Han, Senior Research Officer
Institute of Plant Environment
Office of Rural Development, Republic of Korea
Suwon, Korea

Mr. D. Thomas Hardley, Assistant General Manager
Phosphate Cooperative Company
Melbourne, Australia

Mr. M. J. Hartman, Vice President
Fertilizantes Fosfatados Mexicanos
Mexico, D. F., Mexico

Gen. Hasan Kasim, President
P.T. Pupuk Sriwidjaja (PUSRI)
Jakarta, Indonesia

Mr. Roger Hatch, Managing Director
Canpotex Limited
Toronto, Ontario, Canada

Sr. Frederico Herrero, Representante en Panama
Instituto Interamericano de Ciencias Agricolas
Panama, R.P.

Dr. Carl N. Hodges, Director
Environmental Research Laboratory
University of Arizona
Tucson, Arizona, U.S.A.

Dr. T. H. Huang, Vice President
Taiwan Fertilizer Co.
Taipei, Taiwan

Sr. Pery Igel, President
Ultrafertil
Sao Paulo, Brazil

Sr. Roberto Infante, Executive Vice President
Banco del Estado de Chile
Santiago, Chile

Mr. Robert S. Ingersoll, U.S. Ambassador to Japan
Tokyo, Japan

Sr. Gervasio Inoue, President
Cooperativa Agricola de Cotia, Cooperative Central
Sao Paulo, Brazil

Sr. Gil Itacochea, Vice Ministro de Industria
Republica de Peru
Lima, Peru

Sr. Arturo Jaramillo, Director
Jaramillo Uribe y Cia., Ltda.
Cartagena, Colombia

Dr. Fernan Jaramillo, President
Quimagro, S.A.
Medellin, Colombia

Mr. John K. John
E.I.D. Parry & Co.
Madras, India

Dr. A. Johnson, Program Advisor in Agriculture
The Ford Foundation
New Delhi, India

Dr. Gavin Jones
University of Indonesia
Jakarta, Indonesia

Mr. Arvind Kandappah
A. Kandappah & Co., Ltd.
Colombo, Sri Lanka

Mr. T. Kani, Senior Managing Director
Mitsubishi Corporation
Tokyo, Japan

Mr. Sidney T. Keel, Senior Vice President
International Minerals & Chemical Corporation
Libertyville, Illinois, U.S.A.

Mr. C. H. Kim, President
Pungnong Fertilizer & Industrial Co. Ltd.
Seoul, Korea

Mr. K. K. Kim, President
The Kunsul Co., Ltd.
Seoul, Korea

Mr. Kurt Koch, General Manager
Arnold Otto Meyer Ltd.
Jakarta, Indonesia

Mr. Shinjiro Kodama, Executive Vice President
Sumitomo Chemical Co. Ltd.
Osaka, Japan

Mr. Edward M. Korry, U.S. Ambassador to Chile
Santiago, Chile

Sr. Antonio Ledezma, Director General
Instituto Venezolano de Petroquimico
Caracas, Venezuela

Mr. D. W. Lee, President
Chinhae Chemical Co., Ltd.
Seoul, Korea

Mr. Timothy S. Lee, Executive Vice President
Taiwan Fertilizer Co., Ltd.
Taipei, Taiwan

Dr. Paiva Leite, Director
Fertilizantes do Sul
Rio Grande do Sul, Brazil

Mr. R. A. Lenon, President/Chief Executive Officer
International Minerals & Chemical Corporation
Libertyville, Illinois, U.S.A.

Mr. Enrique Lerdau, Senior Economist
World Bank (IBRD)
Washington, D.C., U.S.A.

H. E. Llach Hill, Ministerio de Agricultura
Republica de El Salvador
San Salvador, El Salvador

H. E. Roberto Fernando Lopez, Vice President and
Minister of Agriculture
Republic of Colombia
Bogota, Colombia

Sr. Jorge Lopez Ona, Gerente
Fertilizantes Quimicos Dominicanos
Santo Domingo, Republica Dominica

Sr. Hugo Luchsinger, Director
Madorin, Luchsinger y Cia.
Porto Alegre, Brazil

Mr. Kenneth Lundberg, President
Agrico Chemical Co.
Tulsa, Oklahoma, U.S.A.

Mr. Gregory Lynch, President
Esso Standard
Fertilizer & Agriculture Corp.
Manila, Philippines

Mr. N. P. Lyster, Manager – Sales Administration
International Minerals & Chemical Corporation
Libertyville, Illinois, U.S.A.

Mr. J. T. Maglutac, President
Commart (Philippines) Ltd.
Manila, Philippines

Mr. R. A. P. Malasakera, Manager – Marketing & Import
Ceylon Fertilizer Corporation
Colombo, Sri Lanka

Ing. Jaime Maldonado
Jefe de Proyectos
Asesores Agro Empresariales
Lima, Peru

Mr. Jose Marcelo, President
Maria Cristina Fertilizer Corporation
Manila, Philippines

H. E. Ferdinand E. Marcos, President
Republic of the Philippines
Manila, Philippines

Dr. Otto Martins Lima, Presidente
Ultrafertil
Industria e Comercio de Fertilizantes
Sao Paulo, Brazil

Mr. T. Matsumura, Director/General Manager
Mitsui & Co., Ltd.
Tokyo, Japan

Dr. Frank Meissner, Agricultural Marketing Advisor
Inter-American Development Bank
Washington, D.C., U.S.A.

Dr. Ruben Meninato, Director
Archilnit
Buenos Aires, Argentina

Dr. Marcio Meirelles, Director
Cia Itau de Fertilizantes
Sao Paulo, Brazil

Mr. Makoto Mihashi, President
Zen-Noh
Tokyo, Japan

Mr. A. Mizukami, Assistant General Manager
Fertilizer Department
Mitsui & Co.
Tokyo, Japan

Mr. G. Mizutami, General Manager
Fertilizer Department
Mitsui & Company, Ltd.
Tokyo, Japan

Sr. Jose Molina, Director
Fertil, S.A.
Mexico, D.F., Mexico

Sr. Alfonso Montero, President
Industrias Quimicas Basicas, S.A.
Lima, Peru

Sr. Oswaldo Tavares Moreira, Manager – Rural & Industrial Credit
Central Bank of Brazil
Brasilia, Brazil

Dr. John T. Murdock, Associate Director
International Agricultural Programs
University of Wisconsin
Madison, Wisconsin, U.S.A.

Sr. Salim Nasta, Director General
Guanos y Fertilizantes de Mexico, S.A.
Mexico, D.F., Mexico

Mr. Le Thien Ngo, General Manager
Vietnam Fertilizer Industry Co.
Saigon, Vietnam

Mr. A. H. Nixon, Sr., Managing Director
New Zealand Farmers Fertilizer Co., Ltd.
Auckland, New Zealand

Dr. James O'Connor, Executive Director
Academy of Food Marketing
St. Joseph's College
Philadelphia, Pennsylvania, U.S.A.

Mr. Ken Oka, General Manager
Fertilizer Department
Mitsubishi Corporation
Tokyo, Japan

Gen. C. S. Pak, President
Chung-Ju Fertilizer Corp.
Seoul, Korea

Mr. David B. Parberry, Managing Director
Australian Potash Research Institute
Canberra, Australia

Sr. Atilio Paredes del Campo, Executive Director
Banco de Fomento
Asuncion, Paraguay

Sr. William Pareja, Director General
Abonos Colombianos, S.A.
Bogota, Colombia

Dr. Jung Moon Park, Chief – Agricultural Production
Ministry of Agriculture & Forestry
Republic of Korea
Seoul, Korea

Dr. Luis Paz Silva, Director General
Oficina Sectorial de Planificacion Agraria
Ministerio de Agricultura
Lima, Peru

Sr. Cesar Parreno, Director
Departamento Fertilizantes
Ministerio Agricultura y Ganadero
Guayaquil, Ecuador

Dr. Al Phillips, Deputy Director
Agricultural & Chemical Development
Tennessee Valley Authority
Muscle Shoals, Alabama, U.S.A.

Sr. Alfonso Pinzon, Gerente Comercio
Monomeros Colombo-Venezolanos
Bogota, Colombia

Mr. Cayetano Pineda, Vice President
Atlas Fertilizer Corporation
Manila, Philippines

Dr. Marcos Polacow, Director
Fertiplan, S.A.
Adubos e Insecticidas
Sao Paulo, Brazil

Sr. Thomas Polanco
Venezuelan Ambassador to Chile
Santiago, Chile

Dr. Walter Pitarque, Resident Representative
Banco Inter-Americano de Desarrollo
Bogota, Colombia

Dr. Roy Prosterman, Professor of Law
University of Washington
Seattle, Washington, U.S.A.

Mr. Erich Pudler, Director
Cia Riograndense de Adubos
Porto Alegre, Brazil

Sr. Ricardo Quinonez, Director
Quinonez Hermanos, S.A.
San Salvador, El Salvador

Sr. Alfonso Quinonez Meza, Presidente
Quinonez Hermanos, S.A.
San Salvador, El Salvador

Dr. Bharat Ram, President
International Chamber of Commerce
New Delhi, India

Mr. C. R. Ranganathan, Executive Director
Fertilizer Association of India
New Delhi, India

Sr. Miguel Revelo, Director
Division Supervision y Control
Instituto Colombiano Agropecuario
Bogota, Colombia

H. E. Duck Yong Rhee
Vice Minister of Agriculture & Forestry
Republic of Korea, Seoul, Korea

Mr. Peter Riddell, General Manager
New Zealand Farmers' Fertilizer Co., Ltd.
Auckland, New Zealand

Ing. Bartolome Rios, General Manager
Fertilizantanes Sinteticos, S.A.
Lima, Peru

Dr. Alfonso Rochac, Director
Central American Bank for Economic Integration
San Salvado, El Salvador

Mr. William Roche, General Manager
Ciba-Geigy Agrochemicals
Singapore

Sr. Marcelino San Miguel, President
Fertilizantes Quimicos Dominicanos, C. por A.
Republicana Dominica

Dr. Antonio Sanchez, Director
Banco Nacional de Fomento
Asuncion, Paraguay

Mr. Ernesto V. Santos, Vice President & Manager
Sugar Producers Cooperative Marketing Association
Quezon City, Philippines

H. E. Pote Sarasin
Minister of National Development
Royal Thai Government
Bangkok, Thailand

Mr. Keith Satchwell, General Manager
Australian Fertilizers, Ltd.
Sydney, Australia

Dr. Antonio Secundino, President
Agroceres, S.A.
Sao Paulo, Brazil

Mr. Neal Schenet, Division Vice President
International Minerals & Chemical Corporation
Libertyville, Illinois, U.S.A.

Mr. D. Robert Schmeltz, Manager
Singapore Branch
IMC (Pacific) Ltd.
Singapore

Mr. Manfred Schwencke, Executive Director
Behn Meyer & Co., Ltd.
Singapore

Dr. H. Russell Shaw, Chief
FAO Planning Team
Ministry of Agriculture
Jakarta, Indonesia

Mr. E. Shirai, Managing Director
Mitsubishi Corporation
Tokyo, Japan

Dr. Paul Stangel, Marketing Advisor
Agency for International Development
American Embassy
Jakarta, Indonesia

Dr. Ferando Suarez de Castro, Director
Instituto Interamericana de Ciencias Agricolas
San Jose, Costa Rica

Mr. Prasong Sukhum, Secretary General
Office of Accelerated Rural Development
Royal Thai Government
Bangkok, Thailand

Mr. Sadikin Sumintawikarta, Director General for Agriculture
Department of Agriculture
Djakarta, Indonesia

Dr. M. S. Swaminathan, Director
Indian Agricultural Research Institute
New Delhi, India

H. E. Arturo Tanco, Jr.
Secretary of Agriculture & Natural Resources
Republic of the Philippines
Manila, Philippines

Sr. Werno Tiggemann, Director
Industrias Luchsinger Madorin, S.A.
Porto Alegre, Brazil

Mr. Tokuji Tonuma, Manager
Fertilizer Department
Zen-Noh
Tokyo, Japan

Sr. Fernando Torres, Director
Icisa, S.A.
Rio Grande, Brazil

H. E. Hugo Trivelli, Minister of Agriculture
Republic of Chile
Santiago, Chile

Mr. W. J. Turbeville, Chairman
Phosphate Rock Export Association
Tampa, Florida, U.S.A.

Dr. Antonio Turrent, Project Leader
International Maize and Wheat Improvement Center
Mexico, D.F., Mexico

Dr. H. R. Von Uexkull
Potash Institute
Singapore

Mr. T. R. Unzicker, Manager Publicity Projects
International Minerals & Chemical Corporation
Libertyville, Illinois, U.S.A.

Sr. Carlos Valdano, Manager
Fertilizantes Equatorianos, S.A.
Guayaquil, Ecuador

H. E. Emilio Valderrama
Minister of Agriculture
Republic of Colombia
Bogota, Colombia

Dr. German Valenzuela, Technical Director
Federacion Nacional de Cafeteros
Bogota, Colombia

Mr. Luis J. Vergne, Division Vice President
International Minerals & Chemical Corporation
Libertyville, Illinois, U.S.A.

Sr. Alvaro Vernaza Herrera
Gerente General Encargado
Banco de Desarrollo Agropecuario
Republic of Panama

Sr. Horacio Vicuna, Manager
Sociedad Quimica y Minera de Chile, S.A.
Santiago, Chile

Dr. Cesar Alberto Vismara, Director
Proyecto Balcarce de Desarrollo Ganadero
Balcarce, Argentina

Sr. Claudio A. Volio Guardia, Manager
Banco Central de Costa Rica
San Jose, Costa Rica

Mr. Heinz Waetcke, Managing Director
Behn Meyer & Company
Singapore

Mr. I. Wakashima, Manager – Fertilizer Department
Zen-Noh
Tokyo, Japan

Dr. James Walker
ROCAP/Guatemala
Guatemala City, Guatemala

Mr. Takeshi Watanabe, President
Asian Development Bank
Manila, Philippines

Mr. Edwin Wheeler, President
The Fertilizer Institute
Washington, D.C., U.S.A.

Mr. K. L. C. Windridge, Secretary General
International Superphosphate Manufacturer's Association, Limited
London, England

Mr. Ko Yoshida, Manager
IMC (Tokyo)
Tokyo, Japan

Mr. Norman S. Youngsteadt, Coordinator – Overseas Marketing
International Minerals & Chemical Corporation
Libertyville, Illinois, U.S.A.

Mr. Frank A. Zak, Supervisor – Audio/Visual
International Minerals & Chemical Corporation
Libertyville, Illinois, U.S.A.

Mr. Jackson R. Zerbst, President
Fertilizantes Fosfatados Mexicanos, S.A.
Mexico, D.F., Mexico

Mr. Doug Zimmerman, Manager
British Phosphate Commissioners
Melbourne, Australia

EDITOR'S NOTE:

*Titles and affiliations of individuals are listed as
shown at the time of their latest conference
participation. All conference attendees could not,
of course, be listed, and we apologize for any
names which may have been omitted.*

PHOTO CREDITS

*xiv: FAO, United Nations; 26: United Nations; 116,
118-120, 123-126, 128, 130-132, 135, Marc &
Evelyne Bernheim; 133: Rockefeller Foundation;
other photos, IMC.*